Childhood

OF FAMOUS AMERICANS

CHILDHOOD
OF FAMOUS
AMERICANS

INDIANS

POCAHONTAS, *Seymour*
PONTIAC, *Peckham*
SACAGAWEA, *Seymour*
SEQUOYAH, *Snow*
SITTING BULL, *Stevenson*
SQUANTO, *Stevenson*
TECUMSEH, *Stevenson*

NAVAL HEROES

DAVID FARRAGUT, *Long*
GEORGE DEWEY, *Long*
JOHN PAUL JONES, *Snow*
MATTHEW CALBRAITH PERRY, *Scharbach*
OLIVER HAZARD PERRY, *Long*
RAPHAEL SEMMES, *Snow*
STEPHEN DECATUR, *Smith*

NOTED WIVES and MOTHERS

ABIGAIL ADAMS, *Wagoner*
DOLLY MADISON, *Monsell*
JESSIE FREMONT, *Wagoner*
MARTHA WASHINGTON, *Wagoner*
MARY TODD LINCOLN, *Wilkie*
NANCY HANKS, *Stevenson*
RACHEL JACKSON, *Covan*

SCIENTISTS and INVENTORS

ALBERT EINSTEIN, *Hammontree*
ALECK BELL, *Widdemer*
CYRUS McCORMICK, *Dobler*
ELI WHITNEY, *Snow*
ELIAS HOWE, *Corcoran*
ELIZABETH BLACKWELL, *Henry*
GAIL BORDEN, *Paradis*
GEORGE CARVER, *Stevenson*
GEORGE EASTMAN, *Henry*
GEORGE PULLMAN, *Myers*
GEORGE WESTINGHOUSE, *Dunham*
HENRY FORD, *Aird and Ruddiman*
JOHN AUDUBON, *Mason*
JOHN BURROUGHS, *Frisbee*
JOHN DEERE, *Bare*
LUTHER BURBANK, *Burt*
MARIA MITCHELL, *Melin*
ROBERT FULTON, *Henry*
SAMUEL MORSE, *Snow*
TOM EDISON, *Guthridge*
WALTER REED, *Higgins*

WILBUR AND ORVILLE WRIGHT, *Stevenson*
WILL AND CHARLIE MAYO, *Hammontree*

SOCIAL and CIVIC LEADERS

BETSY ROSS, *Weil*
BOOKER T. WASHINGTON, *Stevenson*
CLARA BARTON, *Stevenson*
DAN BEARD, *Mason*
DOROTHEA DIX, *Melin*
FRANCES WILLARD, *Mason*
J. STERLING MORTON, *Moore*
JANE ADDAMS, *Wagoner*
JULIA WARD HOWE, *Wagoner*
JULIETTE LOW, *Higgins*
LILIUOKALANI, *Newman*
LUCRETIA MOTT, *Burnett*
MOLLY PITCHER, *Stevenson*
OLIVER WENDELL HOLMES, JR., *Dunham*
SUSAN ANTHONY, *Monsell*

SOLDIERS

ANTHONY WAYNE, *Stevenson*
BEDFORD FORREST, *Parks*
DAN MORGAN, *Bryant*
ETHAN ALLEN, *Winders*
FRANCIS MARION, *Steele*
GEORGE CUSTER, *Stevenson*
ISRAEL PUTNAM, *Stevenson*
JEB STUART, *Winders*
NATHANAEL GREENE, *Peckham*
ROBERT E. LEE, *Monsell*
SAM HOUSTON, *Stevenson*
TOM JACKSON, *Monsell*
U. S. GRANT, *Stevenson*
WILLIAM HENRY HARRISON, *Peckham*
ZACK TAYLOR, *Wilkie*

STATESMEN

ABE LINCOLN, *Stevenson*
ANDY JACKSON, *Stevenson*
DAN WEBSTER, *Smith*
FRANKLIN ROOSEVELT, *Weil*
HENRY CLAY, *Monsell*
JAMES MONROE, *Widdemer*
JEFF DAVIS, *de Grummond and Delaune*
JOHN F. KENNEDY, *Frisbee*
JOHN MARSHALL, *Monsell*
TEDDY ROOSEVELT, *Parks*
WOODROW WILSON, *Monsell*

James
Fenimore
Cooper

Leatherstocking Boy

Illustrated by William Moyers

James
Fenimore
Cooper

Leatherstocking Boy

By Gertrude Hecker Winders

THE **BOBBS-MERRILL** COMPANY, INC.
A SUBSIDIARY OF HOWARD W. SAMS & CO., INC.
Publishers · INDIANAPOLIS · NEW YORK

LIBRARY OF CONGRESS CATALOG CARD NUMBER: 62-16593

PRINTED IN THE UNITED STATES OF AMERICA

*To Garry the sportsman, my
adviser on guns and woodcraft*

Illustrations

Full Pages

Numerous smaller illustrations

Contents

Books by Gertrude Hecker Winders

ETHAN ALLEN: GREEN MOUNTAIN BOY
JAMES FENIMORE COOPER: LEATHERSTOCKING BOY
JEB STUART: BOY IN THE SADDLE
JIM BOWIE: BOY WITH A HUNTING KNIFE
JIM BRIDGER: MOUNTAIN BOY

James Fenimore Cooper

Leatherstocking Boy

Indians on
the Warpath

"I wish I had a gun," Jimmie Cooper said. He looked up from his primer.

His sister Hannah, who was a young lady of seventeen, was trying to teach him his letters. "You don't pay attention, Jimmie," she said. "How are you ever going to learn to read if you don't learn your a-b ab's?"

"But I don't want to learn to read."

"Of course you do. You like stories, don't you?" Hannah asked.

"Oh, yes. But this morning I'd rather be outdoors," Jimmie answered.

Through the window he could see his brother

Will's sailboat skimming over the bright blue lake like a white bird in the sunshine. Beyond the lake, gray mist was rising from a forest of tall pine trees. Jimmie could hear the catbirds and the chickadees making music. He could hear the horses stamping in the barn lot and his dog Frisk barking. And then——

He jumped up. His book hit the floor. "Look!" he exclaimed. He pointed to the lake.

A doe and her spotted baby fawn were stepping from the forest. The doe lifted her head as though she were listening. Then both the pretty animals drank at the edge of the water.

"That's two more for my collection," Jimmie said. "I'm counting how many deer I see this summer."

He and Hannah watched the deer disappear into a thicket.

"I wouldn't shoot a baby deer or its mother," said Jimmie, "but there's plenty of other game.

If I had a bored-out rifle or a shotgun, I could get all we needed."

"Be satisfied with a bow and arrow," Hannah said. "That's enough for a boy six years old."

"A bow and arrow's no good," Jimmie grumbled. "Even the Indians use guns nowadays."

Hannah picked up the tiny book Jimmie had dropped.

"Look, Jimmie. It says right here:

> " 'He who ne'er learns his A B C
> Forever will a blockhead be
> But he who to his book's inclined
> Will soon a golden treasure find.'

Now I'll point to the syllables and you tell me what they are."

"I've a million things I'd rather do."

"Hardly a million."

"You count, Hannah. I want to swim, help Will sail the new boat, work on my canoe, fly my kite if the wind stiffens, take Frisk hunting in the woods—he's going to be a top-notch squirrel dog—and play with Koogah."

Koogah was an Indian boy two years older than Jimmie.

"And visit Mr. Shipman in his cabin," Jimmie went on, "and practice going through the forest without leaving a trace, and count deer and the different kinds of wild creatures. Yesterday I saw wild pigeons, ducks and geese, a partridge, squirrels, rabbits——"

Hannah clapped her hands over her ears.

"And go to the store and watch the trading and get some maple sugar——"

"Let's call it a million," she said. "But you have to study an hour first."

The tall clock in the corner near the fireplace struck ten. With a sigh Jimmie bent his blond head over *The New England Primer*.

Jimmie was hard at work spelling a, b, ab; a, c,

ac; a, d, ad; when there came a tremendous *thump, thump* on the front door.

"Liza will go to the door," Hannah reminded him impatiently.

So Jimmie went straight on spelling. He and Hannah were in the parlor. While he spelled, he kept his eyes on the doorway into the big hall.

Thump, thump came the knock again.

Liza, the maid, must have been at the back of the house. Then he saw her run to the door. He heard a man's voice.

Liza screamed, "Mrs. Cooper! Mrs. Cooper! Injuns! Injuns'll scalp us all!"

Jimmie and Hannah reached the hall as their mother came hurrying down the stairs.

Jimmie felt a little disappointed not to see an Indian in war paint. Only a man from Cooperstown was there. He was Jabez White, one of the settlers. He lived in a log cabin on land he had bought from Jimmie's father.

15

"Some strange Indians have been seen near Cooperstown, ma'am," he said. "I'm afraid it's serious. Likely they're Iroquois from Canada here to join with the Delawares."

"The Delawares always have been friendly to settlers," said Mrs. Cooper, "so there's no danger. Stop crying, and go back to work."

Liza wiped her eyes on her apron and went to the kitchen in the basement.

"Now, Mr. White," said Mrs. Cooper, "tell me about these Indians."

She led the way into the parlor.

Jimmie was glad nobody told him to go back to his work. Indians on the warpath! He felt a thrill along his spine and his scalp tingled. His light hair was very short this summer. "There wouldn't be much of a scalp lock there," he thought, and shivered again.

Mr. White looked really scared. He kept twisting his homespun cap in his hands. "Ab

Dickerson saw Indians with queer feathers in their hair going south toward Otsego Lake," he said. "Ab fought Indians in Canada, and he says these look like the same tribe. They're bad Indians, ma'am."

"I can't believe it," said Mrs. Cooper. "Why, we came here from Burlington, New Jersey, in the fall of 1790. Remember, Hannah? Jimmie was just thirteen months old. That was five years ago, and I've felt just as safe here in the state of York as I did in Jersey. There are few Indians here, and they cause no trouble."

"There was trouble aplenty with the redskins all through here not forty years ago. We'll have it again." Mr. White shook his head. "They don't like so many settlers."

"And Father's in Albany," burst out Hannah. "Oh, Mother, what shall we do?"

"Some of the folks on the edge of the village are going to spend the night in the Academy,"

18

Mr. White said. The Academy was the town hall. "Since Judge Cooper's away, you'd better come there."

"Nonsense," said Mrs. Cooper.

"Ab says we must be prepared. The savages may attack as soon as it's dark tonight. You'd better bring your family and join the rest of us, Mrs. Cooper."

"Thank you, Mr. White, but our house is as well built as the Academy. All my sons are good shots." She put her arm around Jimmie's shoulders. "Even Jimmie can shoot a bow and arrow. Tom, one of the servants, is with my husband, but the others are here. We'll be safer at home than we would be elsewhere."

"I think so, too," Hannah said.

"We'll have a family council of war," said Mrs. Cooper. "Jimmie, call Will for me. Hannah, see if you can find Isaac. I think Dick and Sam are at the stables. I'll send Liza after them.

If the Indians are on the warpath, we must be ready for them."

"Yes, Mother," said Jimmie, darting off. "How I wish I had a gun!"

Jimmie ran down to the boat landing in front of the house. He started to shout, "Injuns are coming," but he remembered in time. A fierce Indian might be hiding near.

He looked around carefully. There was no sign of anyone, but that didn't mean he was alone. Jimmie knew that an Indian could hide so that he seemed part of a bush or tree.

"Hey, Will," he yelled. "Come in. Mother wants you!" Then he whistled as Koogah had taught him. The breeze carried the shrill notes out across the lake.

Will heard and turned the boat. It flew over the glittering water.

"It goes like the wind," said Jimmie, as the boat reached the landing.

"The spar is good," said Will. "It's made of tamarack. That's tough and light."

The new boat was so interesting that for a minute Jimmie almost forgot the Indians. He watched Will fasten it to one of the upright logs of the landing.

"Teach me to sail, Will," he begged.

"Not for a while." Will laughed. "What does Mother want?"

Quickly Jimmie told him about the Indians.

"That's bad," said Will. "You must stay away from Koogah."

"Is Koogah an enemy?" Jimmie asked anxiously. "Koogah's father is making us a birchbark canoe, and we're helping."

"You stay away from Koogah and his father. They're not to be trusted."

"Mr. White says the Indians will sneak in on us at night."

"Just let them try it!" said Will angrily.

"That's right," Jimmie said firmly. "Just let them try it."

Walking up to the house beside his tall brother, Jimmie didn't feel a bit afraid of Indians.

His three other brothers with his mother and Hannah were waiting in the parlor. His little sister Anna was playing on the floor with a fine doll that had come from France. She was too young to be excited about Indians.

"There may be nothing in this Indian scare," Mrs. Cooper began, "but we must be prepared. Dick, go down to the store and get as much gunpowder as you can."

All of Jimmie's brothers were older than he was. Dick, the oldest, was a young man.

"The entire supply has already been given to the settlement," Dick said. "I just came from the village. Mr. Johnson said that Father would want the ammunition divided fairly among the settlers, and I agreed."

"You agreed without thinking of us!"

"Don't worry, Mother," Dick said. "We're well supplied with gunpowder."

"And with firearms, too," said Isaac, the next oldest brother.

"Let the Injuns come on," Jimmie said.

"That's right," echoed Will and Sam.

"I'm lucky to have five brave sons," said Mrs. Cooper proudly.

Jimmie, who was tall for his six years, stood up straight. "Hannah's brave, too, for a girl," he said. "And Mr. Shipman will be glad to help, if we need him."

"Shipman is away on a hunting trip," said Dick. "He won't be back for another week."

"That's bad," Will said.

The rest shook their heads.

Mrs. Cooper looked from one gloomy face to another. "The servants will be terrified," she said. "Liza's brother Joe is the only one we can count on to help. If there's a raid, our safety depends on you boys."

Jimmie took a deep breath and stood up even straighter. "I'm not afraid, Mama," he said. "It'll be an adventure."

All that day the household was in a flurry. Jimmie helped fill the powder horns. The boys put their loaded rifles beside the windows upstairs. Mrs. Cooper directed the servants to shove a tall, heavy chest of drawers against the front door. They hid the silver and a valuable portrait of Jimmie's father that the great artist, Gilbert Stuart, had recently painted.

Frisk, Jimmie's little brown and white terrier, seemed to sense the excitement in the air. He rushed around in circles. He was continuously barking wildly and getting under people's feet as they worked.

"That dog! Lock him up in the woodshed, Jimmie," said Mrs. Cooper.

24

So Jimmie coaxed Frisk into the shed with the help of a bone.

"Don't you mind, old boy," he whispered. He patted the little dog. "Tonight before any Injuns come, I'll slip you into my bed."

Late in the afternoon Jabez White came back. He brought with him his whole family—Mrs. White, his son, who was Dick's age, his married daughter, her husband, and their baby.

"I changed my mind," he explained. "With the clearing around your house and these stout slab walls, I figure it's the safest place in town."

Mrs. Cooper welcomed them. "I'm glad to have three men added to our fort," she said.

The servants fixed a big supper. On the long table in the dining room they put platters of venison, roast lamb, salt pork, and fish. They served wild pigeon pie, baked potatoes, fresh peas, pickles, and corn bread with wild blackberry jam and maple molasses.

Dick stayed on guard while the others ate. He would eat later.

The smell of hot corn bread made Jimmie's mouth water, but he remembered Frisk. He decided that he was not really hungry yet. He could wait. He ran to the woodshed.

The door of the shed was half open.

Adventure in the Dark

Jimmie caught his breath. Maybe an Indian was hiding behind that door. Noiselessly he eased away and into the house.

He got his bow and arrow from beside the fireplace in the big hall. Then he went back and pushed open the door.

"Frisk! Frisk!" he called. He whistled.

There was no answering bark. No lively little dog jumped out at him.

Jimmie ran straight to the dining room. Frisk liked to beg tidbits from the table.

"Is Frisk here?" he asked.

"Look in the kitchen," said his mother.

In the kitchen Liza was hunched over the open fire. She was stirring gravy in an iron "spider" and was trying, at the same time, to keep its long legs steady on the logs.

"Is Frisk here?"

"Look in the garden," Liza said. "He ran out when Joe was getting firewood."

Jimmie ran to the garden. He noticed a lot of animal tracks in the melon patch.

"Rabbit tracks," he thought. The Cooper boys had a hard time keeping rabbits from eating the melon vines.

Then he stopped and examined the tracks more carefully. Some of them were rabbit tracks, but not all. Frisk's paw prints were plain, and they led through the garden to the forest.

Jimmie's gray eyes sparkled. Now he knew where his little dog was. He'd gone to see his friend Mr. Shipman.

He'd gone there twice before. Mr. Shipman

had given Frisk to Jimmie when Frisk was only a few weeks old.

And Mr. Shipman was off hunting, Dick had said. Mr. Shipman's cabin, built against a huge rock that formed one of its walls, was deep in the forest at least two miles away.

Jimmie looked anxiously at the sky. A glow in the west was the only light. It would soon be dark. Then the Indians would creep closer. They might catch Frisk.

Should he tell his mother? No. She was worried enough already. Should he ask Dick or Isaac or Will or Sam to go with him to find Frisk? No. They were needed to guard the house. If he told Hannah, she'd be afraid for him to go. He wouldn't tell anybody. He must rescue Frisk alone! His heart beat fast.

The last of daylight winked out. Armed with his bow and arrow, Jimmie slipped into the elderberry bushes behind the woodshed. He crouched there a minte. The delicious smell of ripe strawberries rose all around him. He hunted in the dark and found a few ripe ones. "My, but they taste good!" he thought.

Then, keeping close to the zigzag fence beyond the bushes, he edged along, out of the strawberry patch and past his favorite hiding place. He passed the fields where the corn was beginning to come up and finally reached the forest. No one had seen him.

"I hope Dick has sharper eyes for Indians," he said to himself.

Jimmie had played in the forest since he was a baby. By day he knew every hump in the path. The air was sweet tonight. He knew the sweet smell came from the Indian pinks blooming in the swamp. Just ahead of him he saw "the chipmunk tree," a pine where the chipmunks often played. Around the turn was the hill where the old woodchuck lived.

Suddenly the tree and hill seemed scary. A branch waved and he pointed his bow. A twig snapped and he looked from side to side. Something moved on the hill and his heart began to pound wildly.

He hid in the thicket beside the path and waited. It was only the aspen clump nodding in the breeze. He went on quietly. He avoided the path and slipped from bush to bush. He was glad Koogah had taught him to do this. But it took a long time—too long. He would never get to Mr. Shipman's at this pace. Jimmie stepped boldly back into the path.

He had nearly reached the cabin when he heard a gentle *pad, pad*. It was the soft sound of moccasins on the path not far away.

Instantly he slid into the bushes. His heart beat louder than the footsteps. They came closer and closer. A branch tickled his cheek, but he didn't move a muscle.

31

Three tall Indians came down the path. In the darkness Jimmie could see great streaks of white paint on their faces, arms, and bodies. It made them look like skeletons.

He made himself be perfectly still, but he wished he hadn't come. Right then he would have given almost anything to be back home. He shut his eyes. *Pad, pad.* When he opened his eyes, the Indians had gone by. They didn't stop or look around. He waited until their footsteps died away.

"Ugh," grunted Jimmie. That was what Koogah said when he was thankful. "I never want to do that again."

He went on cautiously, stopping to listen at every sound. There were many sounds, but they were the usual night sounds, the wind in the pine boughs and in the leaves, and the roar of a waterfall. Sometimes he heard the scratching of some woods animal. There were bears and wolves in

33

the forest, but he remembered what his father often said. "Wild animals are easily frightened. They will never attack unless they are wounded or starving."

They wouldn't be starving tonight, with the strawberries ripe and all the leaves tender and green. If he saw a big bear, he'd just shake his bow at him and scare him away.

A light glimmered through the trees. Jimmie stopped. The light came from Mr. Shipman's cabin! Were Indians in the cabin?

He flopped on his stomach and crept closer without making a sound.

Then something rushed at him.

"Woof! Woof! Woof!" came a familiar bark. Frisk was jumping all over him, licking his face and playfully nipping his arm.

"Who's there?" demanded a sharp voice.

Mr. Shipman, his long rifle ready over his left arm, was in the lighted doorway of the cabin.

34

"Me!" shouted Jimmie, scrambling to his feet. "Me, Mr. Shipman. Jimmie Cooper!"

"Jimmie! What are you doing here at this hour? Come in. Come in," said Mr. Shipman.

"My, I'm glad you're here, Mr. Shipman." Jimmie's voice shook.

"And I'm glad you're here, Jimmie," barked Frisk. Only, of course, it sounded like "Woof, woof, woof."

Hawkeye to
the Rescue

"I WASN'T afraid," said Jimmie. He sat in the cabin door and nibbled a partridge wing.

"I got back sooner than I intended, the hunting was so fine," explained Mr. Shipman. "While I was fixing supper, Frisk trotted in. Good thing I was here. You're a pretty small boy to come so far alone at night."

"I wasn't afraid, much. Except when I saw Indians in war paint," Jimmy added.

"War paint?"

"Bad Indians are hiding in the woods. That's why I came after Frisk. I was afraid they'd steal him. They're on the warpath."

36

"Nonsense," said Mr. Shipman, just as Mrs. Cooper had said. "We have only a few Indians here and they are friendly."

"But strange Indians have come. You must help fight them. Mr. White says they'll try to scalp us all tonight."

And Jimmie told about the preparations the settlers were making.

Mr. Shipman put down his bowl and grabbed the long rifle that he always carried.

"We must go to Cooperstown at once," he said. "This is a terrible mistake."

"But I saw them, three Indians all streaked with white paint."

"You saw Koogah's father and two braves dressed for the Strawberry Dance!"

"Strawberry Dance?" repeated Jimmy, round-eyed. The Indians had looked very fierce.

"That's a religious dance they have in June when the wild strawberries are ripe. They give thanks for the first fruits." Mr. Shipman was kicking ashes over the logs in the fireplace. "Not many white people have ever heard about the Strawberry Dance. It lasts only one night and usually isn't a big powwow like the Harvest Dance in the fall."

"But Mr. White says he saw strange Indians," Jimmie reminded Mr. Shipman.

"He probably did. This is such a good strawberry year that all Indian tribes from up north are getting together for the dance. You know Otsego means 'place of friendly meeting' in Indian language. But that's enough talk for now. Hurry, Jimmie. We must get to Cooperstown before some foolish settler fires on the Indians. Then we *would* have trouble."

They went back much faster than Jimmie had come. Mr. Shipman wore moccasins like an Indian's below his long leather leggings, and he moved as swiftly and silently as an Indian. Jimmie had a hard time keeping up. Twice Mr. Shipman offered to carry him on his back, but Jimmie refused.

"Maybe Frisk would like to be carried, but I'm all right," he said.

At home everybody was running upstairs and downstairs hunting Jimmie.

Hannah hugged him and burst into tears when she saw him. "I was afraid the Indians had caught you," she said.

"The Indians are friendly, Hannah," Jimmie said, pulling away. He didn't like to be treated like a baby. "I knew all along that Koogah would never be anything but a friend."

"It's just as I said in the first place," said his mother. Mr. Shipman was explaining to her. "No danger. Spread the good news to the other settlers, boys."

Jimmie's brothers hopped on their horses and rode through town.

"I doubted if there was any danger," declared Mr. White. "Ab Dickerson is excitable."

"Oh, Jimmie, Jimmie," said Hannah. "Why, a bear might have eaten you, or a panther!"

"That's right," said his mother. "Next time you tell us before you go so far—but it's a good thing somebody went for Mr. Shipman."

Suddenly they heard shouts and the sound of horses galloping.

Jimmie ran to the window. "The stagecoach is coming up the hill," he shouted. "And a lot of people are behind it."

It was like a parade. First came the Cooper boys on horseback. Then came the stagecoach drawn by four horses. It was followed by a cheering crowd of men, women, and children. Most of Cooperstown was there.

"Your father's come. Thank goodness," Mrs. Cooper said.

The stage drew up. Jimmie's father, big and

smiling, stepped out. He was handsomely dressed in blue velvet. He wore a frill at his neck.

The stage usually stopped only at the Red Lion in the village. But Judge Cooper was so important that it brought him to his door.

"I heard about the Indian scare thirty miles back," he said. "We drove as fast as we could to get here before trouble started. So now it's all settled, thanks to you, sir." He held out his hand to Mr. Shipman.

How fine his tall father looked! Jimmie thought. He was almost as tall as Mr. Shipman. Jimmie liked Mr. Shipman's suit better, though. It was of deerskin, trimmed with fringe. Around his waist was a belt of wampum. Jimmie didn't care much for frills and fancy clothes.

"Hooray," shouted the crowd. "Hooray for Leatherstocking! Hooray for Hawkeye!"

"Who," asked Mrs. Cooper, "is Hawkeye?"

Mr. Shipman's thin face reddened. "Some call

me Leatherstocking, some call me Hawkeye, ma'am," he said.

"Hawkeye," repeated Jimmie. "I like that name, Mr. Shipman."

Hawkeye put his hand on Jimmie's shoulder. "Here's the brave boy who came after me," he said. "He deserves the credit."

"Hooray. Hooray for Jimmie. Hooray for Jimmie Cooper," everybody shouted.

Everybody, that is, except Hannah and his mother. They were not so willing to praise Jimmie for his daring deed.

"Don't you ever go into the forest at night again," Hannah said.

"It was an adventure."

"Next time you ask a grownup before you start on an adventure," said his mother.

"Yes, Mama." Jimmie sighed.

A Visitor
from France

"THEN DOWN the path came twenty Indians," said Jimmie, with great enthusiasm.

He was telling the story of his adventure to three boys from the village. They sat with him on the front step.

"You said twelve Indians last time," said Edward, who was twelve.

"You said nine Indians before that," said David, who was nine.

"You said six before that," said Chris, who was six, just Jimmie's age.

"Well," Jimmie said, "you want me to tell a good story, don't you?"

"You always tell a good story," said Edward.

"Go on about the Indians," Chris said.

"I saw fifty Indians!" said Jimmie.

He had all morning to tell his story. There would be no lessons today. An important gentleman from France was visiting the Coopers. His name was Talleyrand. Hannah was busy entertaining him.

So Jimmie told a good, long story. When he finished he heard a patter behind him. There, near the front door, sat Mr. Talleyrand on the high-backed settle. He was clapping his hands. Hannah sat beside him.

Jimmie noticed that Mr. Talleyrand's white hands were almost as small as Hannah's. His hair was powdered and curled, and he wore an embroidered, purple velvet coat.

"Bravo, Jimmie," he said. "You have a wonderful imagination. Someday you will write exciting books."

"Mr. Talleyrand has written speeches that are famous all over the world," Hannah explained. "He knows all about books."

Mr. Talleyrand rose, smiled, and bowed gracefully to Hannah.

Jimmie was careful not to look at Mr. Talleyrand's lame foot. "Maybe he knows so much about books because he's too lame to hunt or do anything else that's fun," thought Jimmie. "He just sits and reads."

"If Jimmie is going to write books, he'll have to study harder," Hannah said.

"Hawkeye told me that the Indians say, 'Much book; little know,'" said Jimmie.

"That's right," said Edward.

David and Chris nodded.

"You must study words," said Hannah.

"Hawkeye can't read words," said Jimmie, "but he can read the signs in the forest."

"Signs?" asked Mr. Talleyrand.

"How to find the squirrels by the hickory-nut cuttings," Jimmie explained eagerly. "Or read a message in the sticks or stones, or track wild animals, or tell directions so he never gets lost in the forest."

Mr. Talleyrand shrugged and lifted his white hands. "Ah, this savage wilderness!"

Just then Jimmie's mother passed through the hall. She was carrying a blossoming plant to a sunny window filled with ferns.

"Not so savage, Mr. Talleyrand," she said. "The beautiful poem you wrote about Hannah will be printed in the *Otsego Herald* tomorrow. Did you know Cooperstown had a newspaper? And Judge Cooper sends for all of the new novels from England for me."

"And did you see our Academy?" put in Hannah eagerly. "It is in Grecian style with Doric pillars. It is lovely."

"You must realize," added Mrs. Cooper, "that

Jimmie's stories of savages and wild animals are much exaggerated."

At the other end of the hall Dick's head appeared in the door. "Isaac just shot a bear in the barn lot," he called.

Edward whooped and dashed through the hall. David and Chris followed. Jimmie started, then turned back.

"Mr. Talleyrand, would you like to see the bear, too?" he asked politely.

Mr. Talleyrand's face turned as white as his powdered curls. He took a pinch of snuff from a little jeweled box and sneezed daintily.

"Thank you, Jimmie," he said, "but I believe not just now."

The next day Mr. Talleyrand left by stage for Philadelphia.

"He didn't like it here, did he, Papa?" Jimmie observed. "He didn't want to stay and try bear steak. What a strange person!"

Judge Cooper and Jimmie stood watching the stage until it was out of sight.

"Why, he had a good time reciting poetry to Hannah," said his father.

"Oh, he liked Hannah, but he didn't like Cooperstown."

"No, nor did he like New York or Philadelphia," admitted Judge Cooper. "Mr. Talleyrand has always lived in Europe. It's difficult for him to understand our new country where freedom is in the very air."

"Freedom?" Jimmie was puzzled.

"In our United States men can work at any job they choose, Jimmie. They can worship as they choose. They all have a chance to own land. When you're older you'll understand how wonderful that is."

Jimmie drew a deep breath. He could smell wild raspberries and roses. The sun was bright and the fish were leaping in the lake. He had a lot to do this morning. He was going to pick berries and fish. Then he was going to practice bird calls with his friend Koogah in the forest. High over the treetops he saw a bald eagle circle and ride on the wind.

"Freedom!" Jimmie repeated happily. "I understand it now!"

Jimmie Sees
the Monster

"It KILLED a dozen of Master Cory's chickens," said one boy.

"It killed six dozen of Mr. Winkelhofer's," said another.

"It carried off a sheep."

"And a calf."

"And a pig."

"Elisha Talbott saw its tracks. He says it must be as big as a man."

"Bigger!" said Jimmie. "My brother Dick saw it, and he says it's huge!"

Jimmie was now eight years old and going to Master Cory's school. On this gray November day, his schoolmates, instead of playing leap frog or ball as usual at the noon hour after lunch, were talking about the monster.

For two weeks a strange creature had been killing chickens, carrying off stock, and scaring people. Some said it was a wolf. Some said it was a panther. Some said it was a monster that the Indians north of the lake had brought down from Canada to prey on the settlement. The Indians had been grumbling because the white men killed so much game.

"If your brother saw the monster, why didn't he shoot it?" a boy demanded.

Before Jimmie could answer, Master Cory appeared at the Academy entrance. He stood between the two white pillars and rang the bell. The boys marched inside.

Master Cory's school occupied one room of the two on the first floor of the narrow, white building. Upstairs there was one big room used for meetings, court balls, and, on Sunday, for church services.

Jimmie thought the Academy was beautiful. He especially admired the "lake fish" carved of wood that was the weather vane.

Today Chris bumped into him as they scrambled to their places on the long wooden bench. Jimmie let himself fall against Edward on the other side. Edward nudged another boy, and the whole row fell over like a row of dominoes.

The gray sky dimmed the light that came through the big windows behind Master Cory. He fixed his eyes sternly on Jimmie.

"If it were not so dark in here, I would suspect that this disorder was not entirely an accident," said Master Cory. "Open your books. Read."

Jimmie, anxious to make up for his part in the disorder, read louder than usual.

His voice rang out alone. The class tittered. He stopped, his ears burning.

The boys were supposed to recite together. They hadn't joined in because they couldn't see the words. Jimmie knew the lesson by heart.

"Jimmie memorizes easily," said Master Cory. "I wish you all had that gift."

Jimmie's eyes widened. "Why, anybody can do that," he thought.

"It's too dark for lessons this afternoon," Master Cory went on. "School is dismissed."

"Hurrah!" the boys all shouted.

Master Cory followed the boys to the entrance. "Now go straight home," he cautioned. "No loitering or playing. I'm afraid a big storm is on the way." He looked up anxiously at the low, gray clouds. "Ah, I hope this isn't the beginning of another winter like the last one."

"I hope it is," thought Jimmie as he skipped down the street.

Last year heavy snow had come in November and stayed until April. The hills had looked like giant snowballs. The lake was frozen over all winter. Every day on his sled he coasted downhill and far out on the ice. With each snow, drifts piled up high on the roads. Children who lived in the outskirts of the settlement were snowbound. School had to be closed often.

A few feathery flakes floated in the air now as he left the street near the Academy and crossed a new clearing. A footpath led up the wooded hill ahead of him.

Usually Jimmie rode his pony, Jet, to school, though after the gallop down the drive, the Academy was only a short distance away.

That morning his mother had said, "If there's a monster loose, Jet would be safer in the barnyard while you're in school."

"The monster is probably somebody's tabby cat," replied his father.

"I'll walk today anyway," said Jimmie. "I want to run my beaver traps after school."

"Oh, you mustn't go into the woods alone," said his mother.

His father laughed, but Dick offered to help Jimmie run the traps. Dick was the only brother at home. Isaac, Will, and Sam were away at school that term.

Of course, Dick didn't know that school would be dismissed so early. Now Jimmie thought it would be babyish to wait for Dick.

"Who's afraid of a monster?" he said to himself, striding bravely with big steps among the pine stumps.

A sudden noise made him jump. Something flashed close. Three partridges, their wings whirring like a roll of a drum, had started up almost at his feet. They flew into the sumacs on the edge of the woods.

"That scared me," Jimmie muttered. "Silly."

He stepped into the woods.

Leafless trees crowded among the dark pines

on both sides of the narrow path. He moved his eyes quickly all around, the way Hawkeye did when he was looking for game or danger. He knew that the path was cut through wilderness that on one side stretched for many miles.

There was not a sound except the click of his feet on the frozen ground. Then came a strange cry. It sounded loud, yet far away. Jimmie shivered and stopped in his tracks.

The cry came again, fainter—then again, fainter still.

"Oh, that's Billy Kirby yelling to his oxen," said Jimmie aloud. He hurried on.

Billy Kirby was a woodchopper. Jimmie had heard Kirby boast in the general store that his voice carried a mile, and he could make it echo from hill to hill along the lake.

Jimmie found nothing in his six traps set in the stream above the beaver dam. Without stopping to visit the dam today, he ran back to the

path. It went through a strip of beech woods to a curving mountain road.

Snow was flying faster. The stillness and the whiteness gave him a lonesome feeling.

"I hope old Gobble-Gobble is waiting for me," he said to himself as he made the first footprint in the white road.

Beyond a turn near a giant oak, a fine turkey cock walked sedately. Jimmie walked faster. So did Gobble-Gobble. Jimmie began to run. So did the turkey, but not exactly, just a jog trot. Jimmie was gaining. He was so close that in a minute he could touch the turkey's tail feathers. It was a wide, fat turkey.

"Imagine catching a wild turkey!" he thought.

He ran faster and stretched out his hand.

Gobble-Gobble spurted 'way ahead. Then with a lazy sweep of his wings he took off. Up, up, high over the treetops more than a hundred feet above, he soared out of sight.

"Good-by, old Gobble-Gobble," said Jimmie. "You're smarter than I thought, and bigger. Why, you're a monster yourself."

That reminded him to look into the bushes that grew by the road.

Through the snow-edged branches Jimmie was looking straight into an Indian's scowling face. His black eyes glittered. He carried a rifle. In his wampum belt was a knife.

Jimmie lifted his hand in greeting. He hoped he didn't look scared.

With a quick thrust of his left hand the Indian signaled Jimmie not to move.

He obeyed. His heart was whirring like a partridge's wing. But he looked the Indian boldly in the eye.

There was a sudden sound of snapped twigs, then a rush, like a breeze. Three deer broke from the woods a few yards ahead of them. The Indian's rifle cracked. A buck leaped high and fell. The other two deer streaked across the road and were gone.

In one leap the Indian was beside the fallen animal. His knife flashed, and blood gushed red on the white ground.

"Good work," said Jimmie. He knew the shot had killed the buck instantly.

The Indian grinned.

Now Jimmie knew why he had scowled at first. He was afraid Jimmie would scare away the game he was stalking.

The Indian shouldered his deer and disappeared among the snow-covered bushes.

Jimmie took a deep breath and went on.

The snow feathers were coming down now thick enough to make a feather bed.

"If the monster came, I couldn't see him," thought Jimmie, "and he couldn't see me. Anyway, I haven't much farther to go." He began to whistle as he walked.

Once past the tall pine that rose above the other trees, he would see the roof of the Manor House, his home.

He passed the pine. Among the motionless, snow-covered trees, a branch of a big maple was nodding and twisting. Suddenly snow fell from it in a cloud.

Jimmie stopped short. Squirrels shook boughs like that, but not such big boughs. This one was as big as a young tree.

He looked around for a weapon. Stones were hidden by the snow. They were no good anyway. He grabbed a big stick and went on slowly, eyes on the tree.

The maple stopped waving, and through the curtain of snow he saw a dark form hunched in the tree. The creature was waiting.

Jimmie set his teeth. He would have to pass the maple tree. Suddenly he flung the stick with all his force.

He didn't try to throw it at the animal. Instead he sent it crashing into the pine tree. The crack of branch against branch rang out in the cold stillness like a shot.

Jimmie saw the maple wave wildly again, heard the scratch of claws, then silence. There was no sign of a dark form. He'd frightened the monster into retreat.

He didn't whistle any more. He needed all his breath, for he ran all the rest of the way home as fast as he could.

"I WANT TO STAY HERE"

"That settles it," said his mother as the Coopers sat around the fireplace that night. "When I go to Albany after Christmas with little Anna, Jimmie must go with us."

"Oh, Mama," wailed Jimmie.

"Civilization will be good for you."

63

"I can't go to Albany," begged Jimmie. "I've been there once. I liked the pastry shops, but there was nothing to do."

"You find far too much to do here," said his mother. "First savages—now monsters."

"But this winter's going to be like last one!"

"God forbid," said his father. "Last year the cold came before the settlers dug their roots, especially the potatoes. They were all frozen. If there hadn't been plenty of game, we'd all have had slim rations."

"But the snow was fun," said Jimmie.

His mother shivered. "A horrible winter! You can't realize it, William," she added to Jimmie's father, "because you were away so much. I can never stand a whole winter here again."

"It wasn't as bad as the winter of '89," Judge Cooper replied. "Washington was inaugurated our first President in the spring of that year. Remember, Elizabeth? And——"

"Jimmie was born," said his mother.

"Oh, was I here?" asked Jimmie.

"No," said Judge Cooper. "All of you were safe in Burlington, New Jersey. Sometimes I thought I'd have to go back there to stay. Here I'd sold forty thousand acres of land. My tenants were to pay me in sugar, grain, pork. But there wasn't any pork. There wasn't anything."

"No corn, Papa?"

"Not a bit. The grain didn't mature that year and there was very little game. The brave fellows who had built their cabins in the wilderness faced starvation. Some of them had their families with them, too."

Hannah passed a plate of molasses taffy.

"What did you do, Papa?" asked Jimmie before he popped a piece of taffy in his mouth.

"I sent to Pennsylvania for wheat and salt. But it was a long time coming. The cargoes landed in Albany, were brought by boat up the

Mohawk, then carried here on pack horses. I was ready to give up the settlement when a big run of herring came up the Susquehanna. I never saw anything like it. We wove a net of twigs and took herring by the thousands. That saved us. The next year was a good one. This slab house was finished, and I was able to bring you all out to the frontier."

"I like the frontier," said Jimmie. "And I don't want to go to Albany. I want to stay right here always."

Good Day
for Hunting

ONE DAY, not long after this, Jimmie and Koogah were shooting arrows at a target on the barnyard fence. It was a sunny afternoon. The snow had all melted.

Most of Jimmie's shots went over the fence into the cornfield, but Koogah hit the target time after time.

"You're a better shot than I am, Koogah," Jimmie sighed.

Koogah didn't answer, but twanged his bow once more. Straight to the bull's eye went the Indian boy's arrow.

Jimmie shot again. The arrow soared just as

67

a partridge rose in the field. Feathers flew, and the bird dropped.

"Koogah, I shot a partridge!" shouted Jimmie, scrambling over the fence.

He held up the bird. "It's a fat one. Won't Mother be glad? Sometimes Dick and Isaac hunt all day with their guns and bring back only two or three. We often have to buy partridge from Hawkeye.

"You good shot," said Koogah. He smiled broadly at his friend.

Jimmie laughed. "Good, nothing. I didn't even know the bird was there, but anyway he'll taste good. Let's go through the field. Maybe we can find another."

Koogah shook his head. "No partridge," he said. He pointed into the wooded hill beyond the field. "Duck."

"Are the ducks settling on the streams? They don't seem to be coming to the lake the way they

68

did earlier. Papa says it's because they've been shot at so much."

"Come," said Koogah.

Proudly carrying his partridge, Jimmie followed Koogah across the fields and into the woods. The trees were bare except the oaks. Their red-brown leaves crackled in the wind, and the pines swayed.

Jimmie wore a cap of homespun dyed with butternut bark. He pulled it over his ears. "It's cold in the forest," he said. "I wish I'd worn my foxskin cap."

They tramped along a rushing stream and crossed a deer path.

"Is it very far?" asked Jimmie. His mud-coated boots seemed to weigh a ton.

But Koogah was bending over, his ear almost to the ground.

"Is somebody coming?" asked Jimmie.

Koogah nodded.

"If they were enemies following us, what would you do?"

Koogah pointed to the water.

"Of course. Our footprints wouldn't show in the gravel. They couldn't trail us."

"Ugh," agreed Koogah.

"But we can't do it today," said Jimmie regretfully. "Hannah'll be cross if I get my new stockings wet." He looked in all directions. He saw no one. The only sounds were the wind and the water. Then he spoke again. "Are you sure you heard footsteps?"

Koogah didn't answer as they plodded on.

After a while Jimmie said, "I don't see anybody. This time you must be mistaken."

Koogah pointed down the stream. There stood a tall Indian.

He was an old man with a blanket around his shoulders. He wore buckskin moccasins and leggings. On his arm he carried a basket woven

70

of peeled ashwood decorated in red and black. He padded silently toward them.

"Indian John," whispered Jimmie. He'd often seen the old Indian in town.

"*Sego*," said Koogah to Indian John.

"*Sego*," echoed Jimmie nervously.

"*Sego*," answered Indian John.

He pulled a knife from his belt of bark, and Jimmie jumped back. The old Indian stooped and dug carefully around some dried weeds.

His blanket fell apart, showing his broad, bare chest. Jimmie noticed a large silver medal that hung from a buckskin thong around his neck. The medal was engraved with a picture of George Washington.

Indian John broke off the tops of his weeds and put the roots in the basket. Then he went on and was soon out of sight.

"What does he want with those old roots?" remarked Jimmie.

"Cure," said Koogah. "Cure fever."

"And what does *sego* mean?"

"Friend," said Koogah.

"And *ot* means place," said Jimmie, his gray eyes sparkling at his discovery. "Why, that's how the lake gets its name! Otsego is both words together. It means——"

He stopped as Koogah pointed to a weed-grown pool a few feet from the stream.

"Duck," said Koogah.

"Why, there isn't a sign of a duck."

"Wait sundown. Duck come. We shoot many then."

The boys broke off pine boughs and built a shelter. Then they crawled into it.

"This is snug," said Jimmie. "We even have a roof." His nostrils quivered. "Do I smell wintergreen berries, Koogah? We even have something to eat!"

They were in a patch of wintergreen. They

72

chewed the spicy bright-red berries while they waited for sundown.

It was tiresome crouching beneath the boughs. Every time Jimmie stretched a muscle Koogah frowned at him.

"But you said they wouldn't come until sunset," protested Jimmie. "There're still three little spots of sun on the pool."

"If duck see or hear you—not come," whispered Koogah.

Jimmie felt the dampness oozing through the wool stockings Hannah had knit. His back ached. He wondered uneasily how far he and Koogah had followed the stream. The wind had died down. The only sound was the steady rush of the water.

Now he remembered that Hannah had told him to come in early that day. "Your monster won't be looking for a big boy of eight in broad daylight," she said.

Daylight was fading. Far away he heard a sound like wind in the tall pine trees. It came louder and closer, more like a buzz of bees.

Koogah pointed upward. The buzz changed to a crackle and chatter. The sky was black with ducks, flapping and calling and scolding, the biggest clatter anybody could imagine.

Jimmie's hand shook as he aimed his bow.

"Wait," said Koogah.

The ducks were still circling too high for a good shot. Suddenly they swooped lower.

"Now," said Koogah, raising his own bow.

But something bumped between the boys, sending Koogah sprawling.

"Woof! Woof!" Frisk had followed them.

Instantly Jimmie collared him. "Down, boy. Quiet!" he ordered.

But Frisk barked louder and tried to run.

Koogah, on his knees, shot. Too late! The

ducks were flying high. In a minute they were black specks in the sky. Then they could not be seen at all.

"You scamp! You ruined our hunt," scolded Jimmie. He had shut Frisk up during target practice because he was afraid the lively little dog would get hit.

Frisk kept on barking in a deep, hoarse tone. Then with a mighty jerk, he sprang away.

"Tree," grunted Koogah.

Jimmie gasped. Frisk was leaping and barking below a big oak tree. On the thick branch nearest the ground crouched a panther.

There was no stopping Frisk. He was frantic. He jumped higher and higher, barking wildly. The panther hunched its back. Jimmie was close enough to see it clearly. It was a grayish-brown color and ten times as big as Frisk.

"Oh, if it springs it'll kill Frisk!" cried Jimmie. "Frisk, Frisk, come back here!"

"We go," said Koogah, as he backed away from the shelter.

"And leave Frisk?" demanded Jimmie. "No. We'll both shoot at the same time."

Koogah shook his head. "Arrow get partridge, not panther."

Jimmie's voice shook. "This is the monster. We can't let him get away. One of us must go for help, and the other stay with Frisk."

"I stay," Koogah said.

Jimmie thought quickly. He knew Koogah was as scared as he was. But if the animal attacked Frisk, whoever stayed must try his arrows, and Koogah was the better shot.

"All right," said Jimmie. "I'll go get Dick."

Koogah grabbed his arm. "No, my brother hunting." He pointed at the gray woods.

"You go get him, Koogah. Hurry. You know where to find him. I don't."

The Indian boy slipped from the shelter and

76

glided away. The leafless bushes seemed to swallow him.

The panther snarled. Jimmie saw his long white teeth. He held his bow ready. He wouldn't shoot unless the animal came down the tree.

Frisk was jumping on one side of the panther and then the other. The panther moved its head from side to side and batted at Frisk with its big paw. Then it began to crawl along the limb. The bough of dry leaves swished up and down. Jimmie felt sure that this must be the monster that had frightened him before.

An arrow through the heart or through the eye might kill it. But he knew he wasn't that good a shot. And the panther was moving so that he'd have no chance to hit it at all.

He reached for a stick. It was moist. The trees were moist. This time the stick would not crack in the stillness with a sharp report.

The tipping branch brought the animal close

to the ground. Frisk ran to the shelter, then back to the panther, barking with a will. He was used to treeing squirrels and coons. He couldn't see why Jimmie didn't take a shot at his prey.

Now the panther's mean little eyes were on Jimmie crouching in the blind.

Jimmie's cold hand tightened on the stick and he got to his feet. "If he comes, I'll fight him the best I can," he resolved.

"Down," said a sharp voice. Jimmie ducked as a spurt of fire exploded before his eyes. He saw the oak branch fly up and the panther hit the ground.

Bang, bang went some more guns. Then suddenly two Indian braves and Koogah darted from the brush behind Jimmie.

Frisk crumpled at Jimmie's feet.

"Frisk, are you hit?" he cried.

But he wasn't.

"He's plain tuckered out, poor fellow," Jimmie said. "He's a mighty little dog to be fighting monsters. Wasn't he brave?"

He carried Frisk home, and the Indians carried the monster. Jimmie didn't forget to take his partridge, too.

"That settles it," said his father that night at the supper table as he picked up a piece of partridge breast. "Any boy who can shoot a partridge with a bow and arrow is certainly big enough to own a gun."

"Oh, Papa!" gasped Jimmie.

"Of course you must have someone with you to help handle it, but we have plenty of good gunners around here."

"But I'll be in Albany all winter with Mother and Anna," said Jimmie mournfully.

"I suppose I shouldn't worry about a boy as brave and able to take care of himself as Jimmie," said his mother. "When he met that dreadful panther he knew just what to do."

Hannah exclaimed, "Leatherstocking himself couldn't have done better!"

"And he shouldn't miss Master Cory's teaching," his mother went on.

Jimmie's eyes shone as bright as his mother's best silver platter.

"You mean I can stay home all winter?"

"Yes," said his mother. "You're such a regular 'Leatherstocking boy,' Jimmie, that I suppose you wouldn't enjoy the capital, after all."

Rabbits and Wolves

Jimmie, carrying a gun as tall as he was, followed Hawkeye across the frozen field. He was having a hard time keeping up with the brisk stride of the scout's long leather-stockinged legs. Hawkeye wore those leggings the year round. Today, however, Jimmie noticed that instead of his leaf-green shirt trimmed with dull-yellow fringe, he wore a fringed jacket of skins. It was exactly the color of the rough, brown landscape.

"Now I know why he wears the green suit in summer," Jimmie thought. "It helps him hide in the forest."

The air was crisp and fresh. Jimmie could

smell wild grapes warming in the sun. Frisk trotted beside him, but Hawkeye's two beagle hounds went ahead, sniffing the ground.

"We'll find rabbits in the stump fences," said Hawkeye confidently.

The field was enclosed by stumps that had been pulled up by the roots and set close together. The big roots, intertwined, made good cover for small game.

Suddenly the beagles began to bay. Their short legs moved faster. Then out of the stump fence darted a rabbit.

"Shoot!" said Hawkeye.

Jimmie raised the heavy gun and fired. But the rabbit kept on running and disappeared into the fence.

"Missed. I should have let you have the shot," said Jimmie. "I've been shooting a year, too."

"I missed a lot when I was your age," Hawkeye said. "You shot quick. That's good."

Hawkeye shot the second rabbit that got up. Jimmie missed the next.

"In target practice once I shot as well as Isaac," said Jimmie.

"It takes practice in the field," said Hawkeye. "Here, I'll load your gun for you."

Jimmie watched him pour powder from his powder horn into a small measure which he took from a leather pouch.

"Now you pour the powder in the muzzle and put in a wad, don't you?" said Jimmie.

"That's right. Next, your shot, another wad, and you're ready."

Hawkeye shot another rabbit.

"This time I'll get mine," Jimmie declared. He held his breath as he squinted along the sight. "Missed it by a mile," he said disgustedly.

"Better a clean miss than a wounded creature," said the woodsman. "I live by my gun, but I want no bird or beast to suffer because of me."

84

He raised his long rifle as he spoke and brought down a rabbit.

"How easily you do it," said Jimmie.

"That's part of the secret. Don't try too hard."

Jimmie didn't try too hard on his next shot, and he killed the rabbit.

"We can get a dozen!" he exclaimed, as he stuffed it in the game bag.

Hawkeye shook his head. "Never take more meat than you can use. Your mother said six rabbits would be enough for your meal tonight, and six rabbits it must be." A deep frown settled on his weather-beaten face, burned almost as dark as an Indian's by the summer suns and winter winds. "That's something these settlers don't know. Some of them keep shooting for fun."

He pointed to the neat fields that lay between them and the wooded hills. "They're cutting too many trees, too. That'll ruin hunting."

"Papa hates to have game or trees wasted,"

said Jimmie. "He won't let Tom put a sugar-maple log on the fire, and last time he was in Congress he had laws made to stop seining in some of the creeks. There's a new law about shooting deer, too, I understand."

"You wouldn't need law if the settlers would stay out," grumbled Hawkeye. "They keep coming farther and farther west."

"Don't worry, Hawkeye." Jimmie felt proud, striding along, his gun over his shoulder, the game bag in his hand. "There'll always be plenty of wilderness. The road ends at the Red Lion in Cooperstown. Papa says nobody will ever settle farther west in York State."

They went on half a mile without scaring up a single rabbit.

"The settlers have come too far already," said Hawkeye, grumbling again. "Hunting's not what it used to be."

Then all three dogs burst into excited baying

and barking. Rabbits popped out of the fence
and ran in all directions.

"Shoot!" cried Hawkeye.

Jimmie shot. So did Hawkeye, and they had
their six rabbits.

The dogs ran down the fence and chased out
more rabbits. Jimmie longed to try his luck
again, but Hawkeye shook his head.

"America is blessed with plenty of everything," said the scout, "but it won't last because

of the settlers. It's not the panthers and the wolves and the Injuns taking too much game. It's the piggish whites."

"Yes, sir," said Jimmie, turning toward home.

"Remember, Jimmie," Hawkeye told him as he said good-by, "hunting's not only for fun. It's for meat. If you want game on the table when you grow up, don't shoot everything you see."

THE WOLF TRAP

Jimmie thought of what Hawkeye had said as he ate the tender, brown meat that night.

"Nothing better than fresh rabbit," said his father. "I enjoy it as much as partridge."

"Beaver tail," murmured Jimmie.

"Beaver tail!" said his mother. "What are you talking about?"

"It's better than rabbit," said Jimmie. "It's better than anything, Hawkeye says."

"If I ever saw a beaver, I'd be satisfied," declared Dick. "They're the quickest creatures in the woods, it seems to me."

"Yes," said Will, "I've tried a dozen times to see the beavers working on their dam in the stream beyond the Point. Instead—there's a splash, and the colony has disappeared before I see even one."

"The beaver makes that noise to warn the others of danger," said Jimmie. "He slaps the water with his long, flat tail."

His mother shook her head. "I've served you boys wild pigeon, wild duck, wild goose, partridge, 'possum, coon, rabbit, squirrel, venison, and bear meat," she said, "but I draw the line at beaver tail."

"Then I'll only trap for skins," Jimmie said with a wide grin.

A northwest wind shook the big slab house that night. In his upstairs bedroom Jimmie snuggled deep into the feather bed. He heard branches twisting and snapping. The wind rose in a howl that sounded like a human voice.

"Sam, Sam, wake up," said Jimmie, shaking his brother asleep beside him. He thought, "Billy Kirby wouldn't be yelling at his oxen at this time of night."

Sam muttered, "Let me alone."

"But listen to the wind. It sounds queer."

Sam sat up with a jerk.

"That's not the wind," he said, and settled down again. "It's a wolf. Now let me sleep."

Jimmie scrambled out of bed and went to the window. It was too dark to see anything except the silver lake and the black of the nodding trees. He heard the howl again. It seemed to come from the other shore.

He crawled back into bed and stayed awake for a long time listening to that wild cry echo through the night.

"Did you hear the wolf, Papa?" he asked at breakfast the next morning.

"Yes. I hope our thrifty friend has his trap set," said Judge Cooper with a smile.

"William, that is no story for Jimmie," warned his wife.

"Why not, Mama?" asked Jimmie. "I read all the novels Papa brings you. I read the *Castle of Otranto,* and I've started *Don Belianis of Greece.* Why can't Papa tell me?"

His mother laughed. "Your father's story of the wolf trap is a very different kind."

"I can add a moral to it, that you'll approve, Elizabeth," said Judge Cooper smiling.

"All right," said Mrs. Cooper, "but don't mention names."

"Oh, a true story. Good," said Jimmie, pouring maple molasses over his corn bread.

"'You know there's always been a bounty on wolves," said his father, "though they've caused little trouble since the fields have been cleared and the cabins finished. But at Town Meeting a few months ago, one of our good settlers made a speech about the terrible danger from wolves and talked us into doubling the bounty. Next day he came into town with seven wolf scalps and collected double on every one."

"He was lucky, wasn't he?" said Jimmie.

"Not exactly," said his father. "It seems he had caught a wolf in a pitfall, and she gave birth to six pups. That happened the day before the bounty was doubled."

"The day before he made the speech!" exclaimed Jimmie.

His brothers laughed. They'd heard their father tell the story before.

"The cheat!" said Jimmie. "He shouldn't have been paid a copper penny."

"Oh, it was legal," said his father. "We might never have known the trick if he hadn't told a neighbor. He's feeling smart now, but he's going to be sorry."

"Why?" Jimmie asked.

"He wants to run for office. He won't get a single vote."

"Good enough for him."

"If you want to be thought well of in this Republic you have to be fair," said Judge Cooper.

"You are always more than fair, William," said Jimmie's mother. "You are generous."

"Maybe," said Jimmie, "that's why everybody votes for Papa to go to Congress."

Jimmie Appears
on the Stage

MASTER CORY'S school was giving an entertainment. The big hall of the Academy was trimmed with pine boughs and bittersweet berries. All the fathers and mothers, sisters and brothers, aunts and uncles, and cousins and friends were in the audience.

Jimmie's friend Edward was on the stage giving his recitation, a stirring speech of Brutus from the play *Julius Caesar*.

Jimmie peeked around the curtains that were made from two of the Coopers' best sheets. He saw his family in the front row. His mother and Hannah wore new silk dresses. His mother's was dark-red. Hannah's was blue. The silk patterns had come all the way from New York, a hundred and fifty miles away. His mother had on long gloves that his father had brought her from Philadelphia. Nobody else in the audience was wearing such fine clothes.

Moss Kent, a handsome young man whom Jimmie admired, sat next to Hannah.

"I didn't know Mr. Kent was coming," Jimmie whispered to David, who was waiting to go on next. "How I wish I had a good piece to recite, and I wish I had a costume like yours!"

David wore a real soldier's uniform, that is, part of it, a faded blue coat that hung nearly to his ankles. His mother had sewed a tuck in the sleeves. David's grandfather had worn the coat at Valley Forge during the Revolutionary War, twenty years ago.

David straightened his wooden sword nervously. Applause sounded. Edward, stumbling over his mother's dressing gown that he wore for a Roman toga, rushed off the stage. He said, "I'm glad that's over. Your turn, Dave."

David went out and made his bow. " 'The Northern Soldier,' by Philip Freneau," he announced somewhat nervously.

Jimmie had heard his friend practice, and he knew every word of the poem. He said the words to himself as David spoke.

After David said, " 'Then rise superior to the foe,' " he stopped. He repeated the line in a faint voice. He looked anxiously at Jimmie, who was hidden by the curtain.

" 'Ye freeborn souls of fire,' " prompted Jimmie in a hushed tone.

" 'Ye freeborn souls of fire,' " said David. Then he went on:

> " 'Respect these arms
> 'Tis freedom warms
> To noble deeds aspire.' "

Jimmie stood up straighter. He thought David's poem about freedom and the Hudson River and America the best of all.

Then Master Cory was folding a worn old cloak around him. Jimmie pulled it over his head, so that his face was nearly covered.

"Be sure to let your voice quaver, James," Master Cory reminded him.

Leaning heavily on a stick, Jimmie tottered out on the stage like an old, old man.

Hannah had helped him learn his poem. No one else in the family knew what he was going to do. But the costume was a surprise, even to Hannah. Master Cory had found it for him.

He began "The Beggar's Petition."

Jimmie saw a sudden smile spread across his father's face. He knew that Judge Cooper had just realized that the lowly beggar was his son.

But this poem was very sad. Jimmie didn't want anybody to smile for any reason. He made his voice as shaky as an aspen.

When he finished, he saw his mother and Hannah take out their handkerchiefs and wipe their eyes. Everybody else clapped hard. He bowed and left the stage.

"Excellent, my boy. Excellent," said Master Cory as he patted Jimmie on the head.

And because the audience was still clapping enthusiastically, the master sent Jimmie back to make another bow.

As Jimmie walked onto the stage, his ruddy face glowed like the bittersweet berries that adorned the big hall.

"Just the same," he said to himself as he bowed low, "mine wasn't nearly as good a poem as David's. A piece about how we love our country is always best."

A Fight

ONE DAY Jimmie came home from school with a black eye, a cut lip, and a bruised knee.

"I bumped into something," he said in answer to Hannah's questions. "No, it doesn't hurt."

"Surely, James, you never fight?" said his mother. She called him James when she wanted to be severe.

Jimmie pretended he didn't hear.

"Oh, a new book!" he exclaimed, hastily picking up a book from the table. He tucked it under his arm and fled upstairs to his room.

That March day had been so unexpectedly warm that Master Cory let the boys have a

100

longer recess than usual. They played until they were hot and tired. Then they gathered around Jimmie to hear a story.

Jimmie told an exciting tale about Indians.

"That's not a true story, is it, Jimmie?" said Edward when Jimmie had finished.

"Some of the things the Indians did in it are true," Jimmie answered.

"But you really don't know an Indian named Chingachgook, do you?" persisted Edward.

"No, I made that up."

"How do you think of all those things, Jimmie?" asked Chris.

"Oh, I don't know. I like to tell stories. Someday I'm going to write a good story like *Don Belianis of Greece*. It will be about knights and ladies and castles and banners flying. The only problem is that I hate to write, and Hannah says I'll never learn to spell. Of course, she spells like a dictionary."

"It's lazy for a female to waste time on learning," said a boy.

The boy was one of an important family in Cooperstown, the Phinneys, friends of the Coopers. There were young ladies in the Phinney family, and they were all quite different from Hannah. Charles Phinney was only repeating what he'd heard at home.

Instantly Jimmie doubled up his fists. "Hannah isn't lazy. Take that back!"

"I bet she never spun a thread or wove a stitch of cloth in her life," Charles teased, grinning.

Jimmie rushed at him. Charles, two years older than Jimmie, though about the same size, considered himself a boxer. But Jimmie's attack was so swift and furious that Charles sat down hard before he had a chance to defend himself.

"Apologize," roared Jimmie, fists clenched.

"Not fair," complained Charles. "If you want to fight, you have to fight fair."

All the boys crowded around close.

"That's right," said one.

"Let's have a real fight," said another.

"Choose seconds."

"I'll hold your coat, Jimmie."

With a stick the boys drew a ring in the muddy ground. Edward was chosen referee. The fighters took off their coats and put up their fists.

"Begin," Edward shouted.

Charles was quick and side-stepped Jimmie's headlong rush. Then he landed a blow that cut Jimmie's mouth.

Jimmie punched him in the chest. Then the blows flew back and forth, thick and fast. Once Jimmie was flat on his back, but he only stayed there for a second.

What he lacked in skill he made up in spirit. His lips were bleeding and his eye swelling when he forced Charles to his knees.

"Apologize," gasped Jimmie.

The older boy flung him off and staggered to his feet. His nose was gushing blood.

"Boys! Boys!" It was Master Cory. "James Cooper. Charles Phinney. I am astonished."

The fighters stood apart glaring at each other.

"He began it," said Charles.

"Aren't you ashamed of yourself, James!" said Master Cory.

"Not at all, sir," said Jimmie. "I am defending my sister."

"Miss Hannah?" gasped Master Cory. "What in the world has she to do with this?"

"I'd rather not say, sir," said Jimmie.

Charles looked at his feet.

Everybody was silent.

"Wash your faces at the creek," ordered Master Cory, "and come inside."

All that afternoon Jimmie stood in a corner with his back to the class. So did Charles.

Jimmie's eye hurt and his lip still bled a little.

"But Charles looks worse," he thought, glancing at Charles out of the corner of his good eye. Charles had washed the blood from his nose, but blood was still smeared on his cheek.

"I'm not sorry I punched him. I won't tell why we fought, even if Master Cory canes me," Jimmie resolved.

But Master Cory was always inclined to spare the rod. He kept the boys after the others were dismissed and assigned both twenty new words in spelling.

"I don't want to know what your dispute was," he said. "I only want you to settle it and be friends. I can't have fighting in my school. I expect my scholars to be gentlemen." He eyed them sternly. "Gentlemen do not fight."

Most of their schoolmates were waiting for them when Jimmie and Charles came out.

"I don't feel that this is settled," said Jimmie, "until you take back what you said."

"I can't," Charles replied.

"Come down to the bridge tree. Nobody can stop us there. That won't be fighting in school."

"Good!" shouted the boys.

The bridge tree was a tree a settler had cut down to use as a bridge into Cooperstown. Only a stump of it remained. Jimmie led the way to the stump. Glancing back, he saw that Charles lagged far behind.

With slow steps he shuffled to the stump where Jimmie waited. "Jimmie," he said solemnly, "I can't take back what I said because I don't remember what it was."

"You said females shouldn't spell," said Jimmie. "You said my sister Hannah was lazy because she can spell instead of spin."

"I didn't mean to say that," said Charles. "I was just thinking. Your sister'll help you learn those blasted twenty words. Mine won't."

Charles's blood-smeared face looked doleful.

Jimmie put out his hand.

"I-I'm sorry," said Charles.

"I'm sorry, too," said Jimmie. "Hannah says I'm too quick-tempered, and maybe I am."

"GENTLEMEN DO NOT FIGHT"

At home in his room Jimmie read part of the new book. It was full of fierce battles fought by noble gentlemen.

He went downstairs.

"Do gentlemen ever fight, Mother?" he asked.

"Never," was her answer.

He knew she would say that. So he went into the next room and asked Hannah.

"No gentleman would engage in a fist fight," said Hannah. "Sometimes gentlemen fight duels. Duels are fought according to rules with weapons, and after the most serious consideration and for a big reason. A duel isn't exactly a fight."

He went out to the stable where his brothers were. He asked Dick.

"Maybe they don't in Philadelphia, but here on the frontier you have to know how to take care of yourself," said Dick.

Isaac, Will, and Sam agreed.

That night Jimmie asked his father.

"A fight should always be avoided," said the judge, "if possible. Sometimes a gentleman is forced to fight."

Jimmie, remembering how his fight started, hung his head.

"If you keep your temper, you can usually settle the trouble without a fight," his father went on. "That is the American way. Here every man, rich or poor, has a vote. If something's wrong, we can vote and change it. We don't have to fight for our rights in America."

"That's what David says," said Jimmie. "His father left France because he wanted peace."

"Mr. Winkelhofer, the German, came here for the same reason," said Judge Cooper. He looked at Jimmie's black eye. "Never fight, son, before you try to settle the matter peacefully. And be sure you have a good cause."

Next day Jimmie took Charles a present. It was a leather sheath for a hunting knife.

"For me?" exclaimed Charles. "Say, that's really a beauty!"

The sheath was decorated with colorful beads and porcupine quills.

"Papa bought it from an Indian for me," said Jimmie, "but I want you to have it."

"Thank you, Jimmie. My, you're generous."

"I'm giving it to you because I was too quick to fight yesterday," said Jimmie. "Though," he added, his jaw tightening, "if you had meant what I thought you meant, my cause would have been good, wouldn't it?"

Charles said hastily he guessed it would.

Digging for Treasure

"THE MEN start digging the cellar for the new house today," Judge Cooper announced one bright spring morning.

Jimmie was ready to start for school. He threw down his book. "Can't I stay and help?" he asked hopefully.

"Oh, Jimmie, what could you do?" asked his mother.

"I could dig, Mama. I'm nine years old now. You're always saying I'm big for my age. I could dig as fast as anybody."

"You may help Saturday," said his father. "But you'll find it hard work."

110

"Maybe I'd dig up a treasure! Captain Kidd's treasure might be buried right behind our barn. Isn't that possible, Papa?"

"I'm afraid the captain buried it closer to the sea," Judge Cooper replied with a smile, "but any treasure you find is yours."

"Really, Papa? To keep for my very own?"

"Anything you dig up is yours to keep," promised his father.

Jimmie urged Jet to a gallop on the way to school a few minutes later.

"Ed! Dave!" he called as he pulled into the Academy yard.

The boys came running.

"Come out to my house Saturday," he said breathlessly. "We're going to dig for treasure."

He invited several others, too.

On Saturday eight boys came to dig for treasure. One carried a large sack. One had a pick, and two brought shovels.

Jimmie led the way through the barn lot, past the barn and stables, to a long oblong hole. Men with horses were turning the earth, making the hole deeper.

"Why, your old house will be smack in front of the new one," said Edward.

"The old house is to be moved down Main Street as soon as the new one is finished," said Jimmie. "Then we'll have the same view of the lake and a bigger front yard."

The boys stared round-eyed at the hole.

"My, it's big," said Chris.

"It's as big as the whole of Indiantown," said David.

"Almost," said one of the workmen. "This house is going to be seventy feet across the front and fifty-six feet deep. It'll be the finest mansion in Otsego County. There's nothing like it west of Albany."

"Papa is having it built like the Van Rensselaer house in Albany. He visits there," explained Jimmie. "Let's start digging."

"If you boys are going to dig, you stay in this corner out of the way," said a man.

For a while the boys made the dirt fly. Those who hadn't brought tools found sharp sticks and dug with them.

"Oh, look!" said Chris excitedly. His stick bounced back as it struck something hard. "I've hit treasure already!"

All the boys helped him scrape dirt from a rusted piece of iron. It looked like a handle, buried deep into the ground.

"Let me pull it out," said Jimmie.

He leaned over and tugged. His light hair stood on end. His cheeks grew red. But he couldn't budge it.

"Maybe it's the handle of a chest," he said.

They worked fast then. As the dirt fell away, the handle stuck up long and thin. Jimmie gave it a mighty yank. He tumbled backward, flourishing a frying pan.

How they laughed! They laughed so hard that for a minute they scared away the robins and sparrows that had been darting in and out, grabbing worms from the newly dug earth.

"Anyway," said Chris finally, "we've turned up the best fishing worms I've ever seen. Let's all go fishing."

"Good idea, Chris," said Edward.

The others nodded.

Jimmie looked at the lake and sighed. "I'd like to fish," he said, "but I'm going to stay and dig for a real treasure."

"I'll help," said Dave.

The rest stuffed their pockets with fine juicy worms and went off to fish in the lake.

Jimmie threw away the stick he'd been using. He picked up a shovel and started to scoop into the dark rich soil.

"Doesn't the dirt smell good?" said Dave.

"As good as the pear and plum blossoms."

Dave stooped to pick up something. "Look," he said. "A stone arrowhead."

They found half a dozen arrowheads, a boot, and a round stone that Jimmie thought the Indians must have used for something.

Judge Cooper came out to see how the boys' work was going.

Jimmie and Dave showed him their treasure.

"This ground was probably fought over when the British were at war with the Indians," the judge said. "That pan suggests that the British may have camped here. There's no telling what you'll find."

Jimmie went back to his digging, though he felt tired. Dave sat down and watched.

Then Jimmie's shovel hit something hard. He moved away two feet and stabbed his shovel straight down. Again it was stopped.

"I've struck something," he said. "It may be a layer of rock."

"Or it may be the chest," said Dave excitedly. He grabbed a pick and went back to work.

"It's made of iron all right," said Jimmie, shoveling and scraping as fast as he could.

"It's round," said Dave. "It's long. It's——" He dashed away, calling, "Ed, come back. Chris! Joe! Treasure!"

The boys came running from the lake.

Edward had caught a three-pound bass. It hung from a string around his waist. "What did you find?" he panted.

"Give me one of the pieces of eight!" shouted Chris.

"Is it really Captain Kidd's chest?" asked Joe.

"No," said Jimmie. "It's a cannon."

The boys yelled. The men stopped work and rushed over to lift a small, rusted cannon from the clinging earth.

"It's an old swivel," said one.

"It'll work, too," said another. He swung the long, wicked nose of the cannon toward the boys. It creaked and squeaked.

"Will it shoot?" asked Jimmie.

"I believe it will," said a familiar voice from behind them.

The boys jumped.

Judge Cooper, hearing the commotion, had come back. He examined the gun. "See," he said. "It's mounted on a swivel so that it can be aimed this way and that. It can be fired. All it needs is cleaning."

"Was the cannon left here by the British?" Jimmie inquired anxiously.

"I'm sure it was, thirty, maybe over forty years ago," Judge Cooper assured them. General Braddock and his British army were defeated by the Indians in 1755, but the fighting kept on until 1763. That was thirty-five years ago."

"You could kill a lot of ducks and pigeons with it," said a man. "One shot into a flock and you'd have enough meat for the town."

"I bet you could," said Joe.

"It's mine, isn't it, Papa? You said before I started to dig that I could have anything I found," Jimmie reminded him.

"Yes, Jimmie, it's yours," said Judge Cooper. "I meant what I said."

"Then let me use it."

Judge Cooper frowned. "What would your friend Hawkeye say if you turned a cannon on game birds?"

"Oh, I don't mean on the birds," said Jimmie. "I mean for something else."

"What?" asked Dave.

"Just wait," said Jimmie mysteriously. Then he stopped for a minute and counted on his fingers. "Today is the first of May. Just wait two months and four days."

Jimmie's father was making a speech from the Academy steps. It was the Fourth of July.

In the hot sun that burned the yard stood most of Cooperstown. Behind the crowd, a few were seated in carriages under arching trees. In the place of honor in front of Judge Cooper were ten old soldiers who had fought in the Revolutionary War. Some of them wore faded blue uniforms. They sat on a school bench which had been brought outside.

Jimmie, on the edge of the crowd with Hawkeye, waved to his mother. She was in the Cooper carriage with Hannah and some friends from Albany. Jimmie noticed that the ladies were peeping over their fans at the six-foot, sunburned woodsman leaning on his long rifle.

"I bet there's nobody like Hawkeye in Albany," thought Jimmie proudly.

He couldn't see his father, but he could see the

flag hanging from a pole beside the steps. The red and white stripes shone bright in the sun. A sudden breeze lifted the flag. Jimmie counted the stars, five rows of three in a row.

"Fifteen stars," he murmured.

Hawkeye frowned. "Yes, and there'll be twice that many if the settlers don't stay settled," he muttered.

Judge Cooper's voice rang out. "Liberty doesn't mean to do just as you please," he said. "As we celebrate our liberty today, we must think of others. For those who come after us, we must save our trees, our game, and the other riches which nature has given to this great country of ours."

"Hurrah!" shouted Hawkeye.

Some other scouts standing under the trees applauded loudly.

Jimmie looked up at the hills, layers and layers of rich green like waves in the lake on a windy day. "There is so much forest that most people say Papa is foolish to worry about saving it," he thought. "But the woodsmen know he is right. Others will, too—someday."

"Now," said Judge Cooper, "let us read our Declaration of Independence. It was written, as you recall, chiefly by our Vice-President Thomas Jefferson."

"Ready?" whispered Hawkeye.

"No," Jimmie whispered back. "Not yet."

"I'd better get it ready to fire." Hawkeye slipped away.

Jimmie listened to the Declaration while he watched Hawkeye disappear into the birch grove near by.

In a few moments, Jimmie pushed through the fluttering leaves, too. There behind the birches was his cannon, shining and loaded. Hawkeye held a glowing pine brand.

"Wait," said Jimmie. "I can still hear Papa.

The Declaration is longer than I thought it was, and he is going to add a sentence. There!"

"And we, too," said Judge Cooper, "on this glorious Fourth of July pledge to our country, the home of freedom, our lives, our fortunes, and our sacred honor."

"Hurrah!" everybody shouted. Jimmie looked through the trees. The veterans of the Revolutionary War were waving their hats. A drum and fife played "Yankee Doodle." The flag leaped alive in the breeze.

"Now!" said Jimmie.

Hawkeye thrust the brand in his hand. Jimmie shoved it into the cannon.

Boom! roared the cannon.

"Hurrah," Jimmie shouted. "Hurrah for the Fourth of July!"

Boys and men came running.

"Oh, Jimmie, how you surprised us!"

"Let's shoot it again!"

Hawkeye already had it loaded. Again Jimmie fired it.

Boom! thundered the little cannon.

The boys cheered.

"Listen!" said Jimmie. His gray eyes sparkled.

Boom! echoed the hills. "Hurrah for the Fourth of July!"

Writing Is
No Fun

"Jimmie, you must write to your father," said Mrs. Cooper one morning.

Judge Cooper was in Philadelphia.

"But Edward's coming to play," said Jimmie.

"Write your letter before he comes."

Jimmie groaned. "This is Papa's second term in Congress, and I hope he never has another," he said, unhappily.

"He misses us when he has to be away so much," his mother reminded him.

"I miss him, too, but I hate to write."

Gloomily, he settled himself at a small table near the fireplace and with a quill pen wrote:

                              Coopers Town
                              March 3d 1800
Dear Papa,
    I take this opportunity to write you as Isaac is
a going directly to Philadelphia. we have got 6
lambs one has died and another is most dead.
Mr. Macdonnald is a going to leave us for Albany. I go to school to Mr. Cory where I write
and cypher. I hope I shall have the pleasure of
receiving a letter from you soon as this letter
reaches you
                         Your
                         Affectionate
                              son
                         James K. Cooper.

    He handed the letter to his mother. "Will that
do, Mother?" he asked.

    "It's a nice letter," she said, smiling, "but what
does the "K" in your name mean?"

    "I've decided to take Kent for my middle
name. I need a middle name, and I like Moss
Kent."

    "When we named you for your Grandfather
Cooper, we didn't think of a middle name. But

126

if you want one, why not take Fenimore, my maiden name?"

"Fenimore. Fenimore Cooper," said Jimmie. "I like that even better than Kent."

"The Fenimores were a fine old family in Oxfordshire, England, and there are no men to continue the name."

"I'll ask Edward if he likes it."

Edward nodded when Jimmie asked him. "A good name to sign to that book you are going to write," he said. "The one about knights and ladies and banners flying. When are you going to write it?"

"Never." Jimmie spread his long fingers. "Even to think of it makes my hand cramp. I have the story in mind, but I hate the pen."

"I know how you can do it!" Edward's eyes were dark with excitement. "Come down to the print shop. I've learned to set type! You can tell me your story. You won't have to write at all."

Edward's father was editor of the *Otsego Herald*, Cooperstown's newspaper.

Play was forgotten. The boys went straight to the *Herald* office. In the back room, Jimmie sat happily among the type cases and dictated a whole chapter of his story.

"Not so fast. Wait a minute," Edward said. His fingers shook over the little square boxes of type. "My, it's thrilling, Jimmie!"

For several days the boys met after school at the print shop.

Then one morning Jimmie gave his mother several long sheets which had been printed on the hand press.

"Why, Jimmie, did you write this?" she said. "It is a good, exciting story!"

"Those are only the first chapters," said Jimmie, "but I can't finish it now. The days are getting warm and I want to play outdoors."

"Of course," said his mother. "But I am proud of this beginning. I'm proud, too, that you signed it James Fenimore Cooper."

A Narrow
Escape

THE MAIN hall of the new brick mansion was a
blaze of light. Candles burned in two glass
chandeliers that hung from the ceiling. Candles
glowed in gilt holders fastened to the wood
frame of the doors that opened into side rooms.
There were lighted candles in the tall brass holders on the mantel. The Coopers were having
a housewarming.

"Not another cooky," Hannah warned.

"Yes, Hannah," said Jimmie, and slid a chunk
of pound cake from the tall cakestand. "This
isn't cooky."

The sideboard of mahogany inlaid with ivory

130

was covered with silver plates of cookies and small cakes. At each end a glass cakestand held pound cake. Sweetmeats of maple sugar, ginger, and chocolate were spread on a set of three tables made of wild-cherry wood. On a small table of light curly maple was the punch bowl.

"Jimmie, you will be sick."

"It's taken more than two years to build our house," Jimmie mumbled, his mouth full. "Why can't I celebrate?"

"You shouldn't gorge."

"If I can't eat, what is there to do?"

"You can listen to the conversation."

Jimmie saw Moss Kent coming through the crowd of guests.

The ladies all wore dainty, light-colored dresses. Hannah's was the prettiest, Jimmie thought. It was sprigged muslin, made in the new style with a rather narrow skirt and a blue sash tied high under the arms.

"Here comes Mr. Kent," muttered Jimmie, "to talk about the wallpaper."

"Good evening, Miss Hannah." Moss Kent was bowing low. "Is Mr. William Henry Harrison here tonight?"

"No, Mr. Kent," Hannah said.

"I heard that you enjoyed his company a great deal last winter in Philadelphia," said Mr. Kent. He frowned down at his shiny black boots. They were trimmed at the top with a band of canary-yellow leather.

Hannah smiled. "As Papa's hostess while he was in Congress, I had many pleasant duties," she said. "Mother doesn't like to be hostess. I found it delightful."

Moss Kent reddened. "A beautiful room," he murmured. "The wallpaper is English, isn't it? What do the figures represent?"

"I've heard that a dozen times tonight," Jimmie thought. He sighed to himself.

132

"The female is Britannia weeping on Wolfe's tomb," Hannah said. "The man is General Wolfe."

Jimmie looked up at the dark-gray walls. An edge of the paper cut off the general's hand. Farther up it cut off his arm. Near the ceiling it sliced off his shoulder.

"Now Hannah will tell how the workmen didn't fit the pattern right." He sighed again.

"Mother was disappointed that the workmen didn't match the pattern better," said Hannah. "See! The general's hand——"

Jimmie shuffled miserably across the new carpet. He was wearing leather slippers that pinched his toes. The white ruffle of his shirt kept getting full of crumbs. When he looked down to brush them off, the ruffle scratched his chin. If his tight, blue-silk coat had been made of fur, he couldn't have felt hotter. Its big, silver buttons hung like weights.

"For once you are going to be dressed like a little gentleman," his mother had said when she ordered the suit from England.

He pulled at the white neckcloth that seemed to choke him, and almost bumped into his mother as she passed by.

"I was disappointed that the workmen didn't fit the wallpaper better," she was saying.

Jimmie went over to the chintz-covered sofa and sat down by his father. Several guests were sitting on the sofa, too, but there was plenty of room, for it was twenty feet long.

"We won't call this the Manor House," Judge Cooper was explaining to a lady. "That is too English. We've chosen the good American Indian name, Otsego Hall."

"But you have a British hero on the wallpaper," said the lady.

"In Wolfe's time we were all British," said the judge. "Remember, he was killed fighting the

French at Quebec in 1759. Perhaps if he'd lived longer, he'd have been an American."

"We have a bust of George Washington above the door," said Jimmie eagerly. "And over there is Benjamin Franklin."

"And who are the others?" The lady looked up at the statues on their pedestals.

The statuary was made of plaster of Paris painted black.

"That is Homer," said Jimmie. "The one with the mustache is Shakespeare. On the next pedestal is a Greek urn, and the head with the laurel wreath, Papa says, is Julius Caesar. Mama says it is Dr. Faustus."

Everybody laughed as though he'd said something funny, and Jimmie felt his face flush.

Yesterday, when the regular stage and three other coaches rolled down the corduroy road into Cooperstown bringing twenty-five guests to visit the Coopers for a week, Jimmie had jumped

up and down with joy. Now he wished they'd go back to Philadelphia.

"All they do is eat, say the same things over and over, and laugh at what isn't funny," he thought as he looked at the smiling faces.

Then, *thump, thump* broke in upon the buzz of voices.

"Listen," said Judge Cooper.

Thump. Thump. Then came a rhythmic *thumpety-thump*.

"It's Indians," said Jimmie

"War drums?" asked a man.

A lady screamed.

Dick's young wife put her hand to her heart. Dick led her to the sofa.

"It's nothing," Dick said. "Don't be frightened, my dear."

"No cause for alarm," said the judge. "Our friends, the Delawares, have come a long way to have a powwow on Council Rock."

"Council Rock?"

"It used to be a favorite meeting place for Indians," Judge Cooper explained. "It's a big rock that juts into the water where the Susquehanna leaves the lake."

"That's about a mile away," said Jimmie.

Dick's wife sat up straight. Her eyes sparkled. "Let's all go to the powwow," she suggested.

"We're not invited," said Judge Cooper.

"Oh, I'd love to see it," said another lady.

"You'll take us, won't you, Dick?" His wife smiled up at him.

"Not unless you want your pretty curls to decorate some warrior's belt," said Dick.

She pouted. "You're trying to scare me."

"The Indians are honoring an old Mohican chief tonight," said Judge Cooper.

"What's a Mohican?" she asked.

"The word means wolf," he explained. "The Mohicans are a noble tribe that came here from

138

the seashore a long time ago. There're very few of them left, though they are close relatives of the Delawares, I believe."

"Then why can't we go?" persisted Dick's wife. "You said the Delawares were friends."

"They're friends as long as we respect them and their customs," said Judge Cooper.

"I wouldn't risk an arrow in my ribs," said one of the men from Philadelphia.

"He doesn't even know that the Indians don't use bows and arrows any more," thought Jimmie, a little disgustedly.

Thump, thump, thumpety——The rest of the beat was lost in the chatter of voices.

Jimmie slipped out of the side door and stood on the portico steps listening.

"I never saw a Mohican," he thought. "I wish I could see the old chief."

In the warm August night, the drum beat came steadily. Then he heard bits of a singsong chant.

"If I were on the lake, I could hear it better," he said to himself.

He walked down the drive between the Lombardy poplars that had been planted a few months before. He went slowly because his slippers pinched.

Thump. Thump. Thumpety-thump.

"Come. Come. Come-Jimmie-come," the war drums seemed to say.

He kicked off his slippers, tore off his long, white stockings, and hid them under a rosebush. Then he pushed open the gates in the brick wall that enclosed the yard, and ran as fast as he could down to the beach.

The grass, wet with dew, and the moist sand felt good under his feet. Moisture dripped from willow leaves as he thrust aside some drooping branches. The willow clump was his and Koogah's secret hiding place. Under the willows lay a big, hollow log.

140

Jimmie put his hand inside the log and pulled out a birch-bark canoe. It was easy to slide it over the sand and into the water.

He paddled to the center of the lake. It was choppy. The waves slapped loud against the canoe. Jimmie stopped paddling. The canoe, made of light ash timbers with a thin, bark covering, drifted north.

The drums rolled even faster. "Come. Come. Come-Jimmie-come!"

"Surely the Indians won't care if I take a peek at the old chief," he thought. "But I don't want them to hear me coming."

Across the lake he guided the canoe and hid it in the bushes. Then he crept along the shore.

There were only a few stars and the moon wasn't up yet, but the southern sky was lighted by a red glow. Jimmie knew it came from fire on Council Rock.

141

He pushed through tall weeds and stubbed his toes on roots. Trees that overhung the water cut off the view. He didn't realize he was close to Council Rock until suddenly a bright scene rose before him.

In the flare of pine torches, tall, young braves were padding in a circle on the great rock. They were chanting in solemn tones. Their bodies were painted, and they wore feathers in their scalp locks. Some of them shook rattles that he knew were dried gourds with pebbles in them. He couldn't see the drummers, but the drums throbbed steadily.

On the shore behind the rock stood the women and children. The light danced on the women's headbands, necklaces, and bracelets.

"Where's the chief?" Jimmie wondered. "He must be in the circle."

Jimmie slipped cautiously into a bed of cattails and waded closer.

142

The drums and chanting quickened. The braves leaped in the air with wild shouts and made their strong bodies spin like tops.

Then the drums stopped. The dancers stopped. In silence the braves were kneeling. Jimmie caught his breath. There was the chief.

His long, white hair fell around his wrinkled face. His shoulders were broad, and he sat proudly erect. The upper part of his body was tattooed with designs in red, blue, and black.

"Ooh," breathed Jimmie. "All that gold!"

Three black feathers in the chief's hair drooped from a band of gold. He wore gold bracelets up his arms. The knife in his belt had a gold handle. His tomahawk was decorated with gold and silver.

"He's the 'Sachem,'" Jimmie said to himself, remembering things Koogah had told him. "And the man sitting next to him must be his assistant, 'The Owl.'"

143

Big gold and silver medals hung from the Sachem's neck. Jimmie knew that kings in Europe had presented them. He pushed the cattails aside and waded closer.

The Sachem was placing his hands on the warriors' bowed heads.

Jimmie felt a tug. His jacket was caught in the water weeds. Carefully, his eyes on the Indians, he got it loose without shaking the cattails much. He remembered, then, that he was where he was not supposed to be. He began to back toward the shore.

The faint rustle of the cattails was the only sound. He had put one foot on firm ground when—*plop!*—the splash in the silent night sounded like a man overboard. One of the big buttons of his coat had fallen in the lake.

He saw the braves leap to their feet and whirl around. He heard their savage whoop.

Jimmie scuttled through the weeds and

144

straight into the forest. From bush to bush, he slipped as fast and noiselessly as possible. Finally he stopped, out of breath. All he heard was the roaring in his ears. Maybe they hadn't followed him after all.

He turned north, limping, for the roots cut his feet. He was within sight of the bushes where he'd put the canoe when he saw an Indian glide from a tree ahead of him.

A shiver streaked up his spine and prickled into his hair. While he was going into the forest, the Indian had taken the shorter way along the shore. Now the Indian was between Jimmie and the canoe.

Jimmie stood still. "After all, I've done nothing very bad," he told himself. "I'll tell him who I am and why I've come."

He took one step. A twig snapped. At the same moment the moon thrust its round face over the trees. Jimmie saw another Indian.

146

Both Indians snatched knives from their wampum belts and whirled toward him. The knives glittered in the moonlight.

Jimmie plunged back into the woods. He ran as hard as he could. There was no doubt about it this time. The two savages were after him.

"If I can only reach the cave!" he thought. "They're strangers, I can tell by their feathers. Maybe they don't know the cave."

The opening in the great rock in his path looked like a shadow. Panting, he reached it and stepped inside.

He watched the Indians run by, and drew a deep breath.

Cautiously he edged from the cave. Were those shadows on his right fluttering leaves?

Jimmie blinked. A tall figure had appeared and disappeared. "The Indians are coming back," he said to himself.

Keeping flat against the rock, he retreated into

the cave. It was completely dark inside. He waited, huddled against the rock. His heart thumped loud.

The two Indians were at the entrance. They were talking and pointing into the cave.

Jimmie turned and stared into the blackness. He bumped into rocks and skinned his knees, but he scrambled on.

"Maybe they think I wasn't respecting their customs when I spied on them," he thought. His hands felt like ice.

In some places he had to climb over huge rocks. For what seemed like hours he struggled in the darkness. Finally he found himself in a narrow passage.

He put out his hands. A wall of rock rose close to his shoulders on both sides. A rock barred his path. "I'm caught," he muttered. He'd been in the dark so long he could even see the rocks that trapped him.

He looked up in despair and clapped a hand over his mouth to keep from shouting. The moon shone above him. He'd reached another opening to the outside.

Nimble as a squirrel, he swung himself over the rocks and out of the cave. He crept noiselessly around the mound of rocks and saw the two Indians still guarding the other entrance. Below lay the shining mirror of the lake, silver in the moonlight.

Jimmie eased through the trees and reached the shore safely. He dropped into the canoe as it touched the water. Then with swift strokes he shot the light boat across the lake.

A few minutes later he fished his slippers and long stockings from under the rosebush.

Through the open window he heard his mother's voice. "I was disappointed that the workmen didn't fit the wallpaper——"

Jimmie limped around to the back of the

house. His favorite cat rubbed up against him. Frisk leaped and barked. A hound puppy waddled to meet him.

Jimmie crossed the barnyard with the animals following. He and Sam were going to sleep on pallets on the floor of the new shed so that the guests could have their room.

"I'm glad it's the animals that came to meet me instead of Mama and Hannah," thought Jimmie, tearing off his torn, wet clothes. "I'm sure I was never meant to be a little gentleman."

Another Party

NEXT MORNING it was so dark when Jimmie wakened that he thought he was in the cave. He sat up and saw a square patch of gray through the window of his bedroom.

"Cloudy," he muttered.

"What a shame!" said Sam, without opening his eyes. "If it rains, the party at the lake will be spoiled."

Jimmie went to the door. "There's light in the east," he said. "Let's take a swim and see the sunrise over the lake. I'll race you."

Sam leaped up. "Grab your clothes. We can dress on the shore when we come out."

151

Jimmie reached the lake first.

"It's those long legs of yours," panted Sam. "I'm older than you, but you're taller. It just isn't fair."

"Mama says I'll be as tall as Dick," said Jimmie, diving. "He's six feet."

"You will be, too." Sam dived.

"The sky's a lot lighter," said Jimmie.

"Look at the reflection."

The shore was a jagged line between duplicate scenes. The trees, hills, and bright clouds were every bit as clear in the lake water as the real objects above it.

"No wonder the scouts call Lake Otsego the Glimmer Glass!" Jimmie commented.

The boys watched the sun burst through the clouds. Then they scrambled out of the water and dressed among the birches. Jimmie noticed that the sun tinged the white tree trunks around them pink and gold.

152

"It'll be a fine day for the lake picnic after all," he said.

That afternoon the whole party from Otsego Hall was taken up the lake to Three Mile Point. Two sailboats led the flotilla. Three flat-bottomed skiffs were rowed, and there were six canoes besides Jimmie's.

The men carried fishing tackle. A few took guns. The ladies protected their faces from the sun by chip-straw bonnets trimmed with lace, flowers, and ribbons.

Jimmie paddled steadily in the stern of his canoe. Sam was in front. A sudden breeze ruffled Jimmie's hair and sent ripples scampering across the glittering lake.

"Oh," said a lady. "See that little Indian boat toss in the wind. Is it safe?"

"Perfectly safe," Judge Cooper assured her. "I crossed Oneida once in a canoe. And those boys can paddle like Indians."

"This is really a bubble of a boat, Jimmie," Sam said admiringly.

"Yes, it's fun to paddle when the wind makes it harder," said Jimmie. "I like the water as much as the forest, don't you, Sam? Someday I'm going to sea."

As they approached Three Mile Point, they could hear ladies exclaiming over the blue lake, the deep curves of the shore, and the thick green woods.

"What would they say if they could see the Point when the wild roses are in bloom?" observed Sam.

"Or earlier in spring," said Jimmie. "I've found wild honeysuckle there—and pitcher plants, Solomon's seal, lady's slippers, and violets by the million."

"Fishing will be good today," said Sam.

"It better be," Jimmie replied. "Papa's going to make the chowder himself!"

A lady's voice floated back to them as a skiff was pulled to the shore. "Oh, the peace of this wild spot! The utter stillness!"

As if in answer, hoarse barking echoed across the lake. There came a sound of crashing boughs, and a young fawn burst through the trees and leaped into the water.

"Hawkeye's dogs are after him," exclaimed Jimmie. "There's old Hector."

Hector, a big hound, and a smaller dog rushed down the hill, baying. They stopped at the shore, but their bloodthirsty howls grew more and more frantic.

The terrified fawn swam toward the boats, saw his new enemies, and changed his course.

"He can't get across. The lake's almost a mile wide here," said Sam.

The little animal was already weakening. The two boys saw him struggle, sink, and then rise again feebly.

"Poor little fellow," said Jimmie. "Let's rescue him before it's too late."

He called to Will and Isaac to bring up a skiff. Jimmie paddled toward the fawn.

The animal's eyes were wide with terror, but his movements were feeble. Jimmie reached him and seized him by the back of the neck.

"Put him in our boat," said Will. "The canoe's too light."

As Jimmie's hand tightened, the fawn kicked up a whirlpool. Over the side of the canoe and into the lake went Jimmie. Sam managed to keep the canoe afloat.

Jimmie came up, still holding the limp animal. The boys lifted the fawn into the skiff and gave a hand to Jimmie.

"He's dead," said Will.

"I expect he had a terrific race before he hit the water," said Isaac.

Jimmie was running his hand over the fawn.

"He isn't dead, but he isn't far from it. Get something to wrap him in."

Someone tossed the boys a coat, and Jimmie wrapped it carefully around the fawn. He felt the animal quiver.

"I'm going to take him home now," he said.

The party was in an uproar. One lady kept screaming, "I thought the child would drown." Some clamored to see the fawn. The gentlemen were making jokes about "fishing" for deer.

"These noisy people will scare him to death," said Jimmie.

"Just let him loose in the woods," said Isaac. "He'll be all right."

"He won't unless I take care of him," said Jimmie. "He needs me."

"Row back three miles?" complained Isaac.

"And miss the fishing?" said Sam.

"I'm going to take him home," said Jimmie firmly. His jaw was set.

"I'll help." Sam sighed.

"No, I will," said Isaac.

"I'll take you in my sailboat," said Will.

"Thank you," said Jimmie. "I'll go alone."

In the end, Will took him in the sailboat.

The little fawn lay on straw in the barn and drank the milk Jimmie offered him. When the boy stroked his smooth head, he looked up at him with trusting eyes.

"You do have a way with animals, Jimmie," said Will.

"He's such a baby," said Jimmie. "But he's going to be all right."

They closed the stable door carefully to keep out the dogs, and sailed back to the picnic.

The evening star was shining in a deep blue sky as they came near the Point. The servants had built a big fire. A great pot of fish chowder hung over the fire, and Judge Cooper himself was stirring it. Mrs. Cooper and Hannah were putting their best home-made pickles on serving plates. Jimmie saw plump melons cooling in the shallows of the lake.

"Is the fawn alive?" floated out to them.

"How's the little deer?"

"Fine," they both shouted.

"What are you going to do with him, Jimmie?" a lady asked, after they'd joined the party and told of the fawn's recovery.

"I've had several wild pets," said Jimmie. "I've had two coons, a crow, and a cub. But this is the first time I've had a fawn. I'm going to keep him for a pet."

A FUNNY STORY

"Judge Cooper, how did you happen to come out to the frontier?" asked a lady. The feast was over. Everybody was sitting around the fire, talking and relaxing.

"Oh, I'd bought a tract of over forty thousand acres and I wanted to see it," said the judge.

"Tell about being lost in the forest, Papa, that first night," said Jimmie.

"Oh, did you come alone?"

"Alone, on horseback," said Judge Cooper. "That was in 1785, four years before Jimmie was born. At home in Burlington, New Jersey, and in Albany, too, everybody talked about the friendly Indians and good hunting here. I expected to find hunters, both redskins and whites, camped all along the Mohawk. I traveled all day without seeing a soul."

"Was it this time of year?"

"No, it was a glorious day in autumn. The grass in the Cherry Valley was still green, but sumacs were red. Purple asters were in bloom. In the forest the maples glowed like candles among the dark pines. I was so delighted with the scenery that I went on until I was lost. Trees

161

grew thick on every side, and I had no more idea of where I was than the rabbits that ran by."

"Couldn't you tell by the sun, Judge Cooper?" suggested a man.

"The sun was under a cloud by late afternoon."

"Moss on the north of the trees?"

"I didn't know about moss then." The judge chuckled. "I was no woodsman."

"Hawkeye could tell by the stars," Jimmie put in quickly.

"It was too early for stars. Anyway, I'd never studied them. I was lost, three hundred miles from home, extremely hungry, and without food of any kind."

"What did you do?"

"I climbed a tree and got my first glimpse of the lake. I'll show you the spot on the way home. We call it Mount Vision. A bear and her cub were drinking from the lake."

He waited, while people exclaimed.

162

"A bear! How dreadful!"

"Weren't you terrified?"

"On the contrary," Judge Cooper answered. "The two trusting creatures encouraged me. I caught trout from the brook and roasted them in ashes. I laid me down to sleep in my watch coat, nothing but the wilderness about me. In the morning I reached Shipman's cabin. I spent the second night with him."

"Oh, Judge Cooper, you should write a book about your experiences," a lady said.

"I have, though I seriously doubt if it will ever be published. I've called it 'A Guide to the Wilderness.'"

"Were you anxious to see the wilderness, too, Elizabeth?" asked the young lady who sat next to Mrs. Cooper.

Elizabeth Cooper and her husband exchanged quick glances.

"My husband had to persuade me," she said.

Then they both burst into laughter.

"What's so funny, Papa? Tell us, please," begged Jimmie.

"Well, the wagons were securely packed for the trip west. The servants and you children were all in your places. Liza was holding you on her lap, Jimmie."

"Where was I?" asked little Anna.

"You weren't born yet, dear. Jimmie was thirteen months old, the baby of the family. We were ready to start when your mother plumped down in an armchair and said she wouldn't go."

"In Burlington we had a good house close to the street, next door to the Lawrences," said Mrs. Cooper. "You know, the parents of young James Lawrence. The thought of leaving our home and our friends for the frontier——" She broke off shivering.

"What changed your mind?"

"Nothing," she said.

164

"I picked up the armchair with my wife in it and put it on the wagon!" said Judge Cooper.

Mrs. Cooper laughed as hard as anybody.

"Well, I never heard that before," said Jimmie. "Oh, Mama, aren't you glad he did it?"

EVERYONE AGREES

Three days later Mrs. Cooper was showing the guests her flower garden.

"So many varieties!" exclaimed a man.

"Of flowers or pets?" asked Judge Cooper, pointing toward the barnyard.

Jimmie was crossing the yard. Frisk leaped at his side. Behind him came an old striped cat, three kittens—black, yellow, and striped—a hen, a hound puppy, a goose, and at the end of the procession trotted the little fawn.

"If the pigs weren't in the pen, they'd be following him, too!" His mother laughed.

"Jimmie loves animals and the outdoor life here so much that it's a shame to take him away from it," said Judge Cooper.

"All his brothers went away to school," said Mrs. Cooper. "Jimmie must have the same opportunity to learn."

"Of course," said Hannah quickly.

"Of course," said Judge Cooper slowly.

"Of course," echoed all the guests at Otsego Hall. "Of course!"

Voyage of Discovery

ONE BRIGHT morning not long after this, Jimmie sat beside a farmer on a big wagon loaded with wheat. They were bumping over the corduroy road that led from Cooperstown to the Great Western Turnpike. It was August, 1800.

"Papa noticed that this wagon is named 'Collumbus,'" Jimmie said. "Hannah said it wasn't spelled right, but anyway the name makes this my voyage of discovery."

"Ah, boy, there's plenty for you to discover. Wait until we reach the Great Western Turnpike. You'll see more wagons than you have ever seen in your whole life."

"You have to be a good driver to manage a team on the Turnpike, don't you?"

"You certainly do," the farmer agreed. "It's crowded both ways, a wonderful sight. It stretches sixty miles from the Cherry Valley to the Hudson, with bridges, tollgates, and a tavern every mile all the way to Albany."

"I'll be in Albany a long time," Jimmie said. "I'll live at the Rectory of St. Peter's Church. Dr. Thomas Ellison has a school there. He isn't a doctor for sick people. He's a minister and graduated from Oxford University in England. William Jay is one of his pupils, too."

"Any kin to Governor Jay?"

"His son. Hannah says Dr. Ellison will teach us Greek, but Papa says he'll be satisfied if he teaches me to write English."

"I never had any use for either," the farmer said. "Figure you'll be getting homesick?"

"I hate to leave my pets, but I know they'll be

well taken care of. And the lake and the forest will wait for me." Jimmie broke off, biting his lip. "I'd hate it worse," he added slowly, "if Koogah wasn't going away, too. His family is moving out to the Ohio Country."

"Good riddance," grunted the farmer, but Jimmie didn't hear him.

A tall, slim young Indian had stepped from the bushes into the road ahead.

"It's Koogah," cried Jimmie, "to see me off. Please stop!" He tore off his cap and waved.

Koogah's face was expressionless. When the wagon drew near, he flung up his hand in one swift movement. Then he disappeared into the undergrowth by the road.

Jimmie looked back through a blur of tears. The Ohio Country was deep in the wilderness, hundreds of miles away. He might never see Koogah again.

The farmer stopped the wagon.

"Go on," Jimmie said. "Koogah is gone."

"I stopped to pick up that dead porcupine. See it there by the road. My little girl likes to weave quill baskets the way the Indians do. You can hold the horses."

Jimmie took the reins quickly and slid into the driver's seat.

"Be careful," Jimmie called, as the farmer stooped over the motionless ball of prickles. "It may not be dead."

The farmer answered with a howl of pain. His hand looked like a pincushion stuck full of pins. The porcupine moved on slowly.

Jimmie helped pull out the quills one by one. It took a long time. The farmer's hand was swelling quickly.

"Your hand will be as big as a puffball mushroom," Jimmie said.

"I can't use it. It hurts so that I feel sick," the farmer groaned. "What shall we do?"

"I can drive," Jimmie said eagerly.

"Not when we reach the Turnpike, and we're nearly there."

"I've driven the team hitched to our sleigh lots of times," the boy said.

"It takes two strong hands to guide a team on the Turnpike," the farmer added weakly.

"Mine are strong," Jimmie argued.

The farmer looked down at his puffed-up hand and groaned. "Go ahead."

Driving on the lonely road was easy, but soon Jimmie heard the brisk *thud, thud* of horses' hoofs, the rattle and clatter of wagons.

"There's the Great Turnpike!" the farmer exclaimed, forgetting all about his hand.

"My goodness!" Jimmie gasped. "Look at all the corn and wheat. Five, ten, fifteen—why, there're twenty-five wagons in that string."

"Look the other way. Here comes a fleet from Albany. See all those boxes. They're full of silk

172

and calico and coffee and spice. There must be thirty wagons. Think you can handle the horses on a road like that?"

One of the horses tossed his head.

Jimmie tightened the reins as he watched the wagons stream by.

"You have to grab your chance to turn in there." The farmer frowned anxiously.

A stage drawn by six horses followed the wagon fleet.

"Hello! Hello!" the stage driver shouted.

"Hello! Hello!" Jimmie shouted back.

He clucked to the horses, cracked his whip. The wagon swung onto the great Turnpike.

Jimmie's eyes shone. He sat up straight and drove with a firm hand. Albany and new adventures were before him.

Cooper, the Author

It was 1819, just nineteen years after Jimmie Cooper started on his voyage of discovery.

In a buff and blue uniform, a sword at his side, ·and a cocked hat in his hand, James Cooper made a sweeping bow to his wife.

"Governor Clinton's aide, at your service, madam," he said, his eyes twinkling.

Sue Cooper dimpled. "Your uniform fits beautifully, dear," she said. Then she ran to the stairway and called, "Girls, come to see your papa in his new uniform. He'll be the handsomest officer in the review."

Four curly heads popped over the banister.

"Hurry, Papa," said the oldest girl. "Bullhead is prancing. We can see him from the window."

James kissed his wife, waved his hat to the children, and rushed out to his stamping horse.

"Don't forget to meet the sloop," Sue called as he swung into his saddle.

Three times a week, a sloop loaded with merchandise came from New York City, twenty-five miles away.

Watching him gallop down the drive, Sue Cooper shaded her eyes with her hand.

The hill on which their house stood sloped gently to Long Island Sound. The Sound shimmered this morning with spangles of sunlight and was dotted with white sails. The young Coopers lived not far from Scarsdale in Westchester County.

"So many boats," Sue thought. "It's a good view for James. I was afraid he'd find the farm dull after the excitement of navy life under Captain Lawrence, but he likes it. Being an aide with his title 'Colonel' is fun for him, too."

Late that afternoon Colonel Cooper returned. His saddlebags bulged.

"Something for everyone," he said. "Here're silk, calico, tea, sugar, sweetmeats, and sweetest of all, Sue, a book! The sloop met the packet from England yesterday."

"Good. I hope it's a Waverley novel."

"No. It's by an English woman."

"You must read it to me tonight."

As soon as the children were in bed that night, Sue curled up on the couch. James settled himself in his armchair and began to read.

At the end of the second page, Sue hid a yawn. Another page and she blinked to keep her eyes from closing. Then she yawned again.

He stopped, frowning. "This book is a confounded bore," he exploded.

"Go on. Maybe it will improve."

176

He finished the chapter. Then he threw down the book. "Why, I could write a better book myself!" he said confidently.

Sue shook with laughter. "You, who hate to write even a letter!"

"I used to tell capital stories." He jumped up and began to stride the length of the room. "I have plenty of good ideas. Of course I could write a book!"

"Very well then," teased Sue, "why don't you try, dear?"

"All right," said James Cooper. "I will!"

INSPIRATION

A little more than a year later the Coopers were visiting their friends, the Jays. The Jays' spacious home was at Bedford, a pleasant drive in the gig from Scarsdale.

"James, I understand that your novel *Precau-*

tion has been republished in England," old John Jay said.

The Coopers and the Jays were sitting on the wide, wisteria-covered porch.

"Yes," James answered. "It came out in London on the twenty-fifth of August. It has been a moderate success."

"But you wrote about England," said John Jay. "You should write about America. That would be much more interesting."

During the afternoon the old man entertained the Coopers as usual with his recollections of the Revolution and the early days of the Republic. On this particular day he talked especially of the marvelous deeds of a daring American spy he had known.

When he finished, James Cooper said eagerly, "I'm going to write another book, John. "It'll be a patriotic American book. I'm going to call it 'The Spy."

The four little Cooper girls leaned from a second-story window at 345 Greenwich Street, New York City.

"Oh, see the flags!" exclaimed the oldest girl, Susan Augusta.

"And the garlands!" said Cally.

"And the crowds!" said Charlotte.

"I think I hear a band," said Mrs. Cooper. She was holding their little brother Paul.

"Is it all for Papa?" asked Fan, the youngest girl. "Is it, Mama?"

"No, darling, no," said Mrs. Cooper, laughing. "The celebration isn't for Papa at all. It's for the opening of the Erie Canal."

It was the autumn of 1825. James Cooper had moved his family to the city a year before. He was a successful author now and wanted to be near his publishers.

"What's the Erie Canal?" asked Fan.

"It's a great waterway that's been dug to connect Lake Erie with the Hudson River."

"Oh," said Fan, her mouth drooping.

"But Papa will be in the parade, dear," Mrs. Cooper assured her.

Fan smiled again.

"Boom," exclaimed Cally. "There goes a cannon. What does that mean?"

"That means the barges that have gone through the canal have reached New York harbor," explained her mother. "The trip from Buffalo has taken nine days. What a great day for Governor Clinton! He's worked twenty years for this. He is on the first boat that went through the canal."

"Will we see the boats?"

"Papa will take you to see them later. They are all decorated. One of them is called Noah's Ark. It has a bear, two fawns, two eagles, and two Indians on board."

180

"Will the parade come soon?" demanded Charlotte.

"Here it comes!" shrieked Cally.

Down the street glittered a mass of scarlet and gold.

"Is Papa in that?" asked Fan.

"No, that's the Fire Department leading the parade.

Fine big horses pulled the fire engines. Wagons decorated with autumn leaves, banners, and flowers rolled by. Bands played. Soldiers and sailors marched. Cavalrymen sat astride prancing horses. Men dressed for work rode in the decorated wagons or passed on foot. Some of them carried gay banners.

"Every trade is represented in this parade," said Mrs. Cooper. "There has been a celebration in Albany and other places along the canal, but nothing to compare with this, I'm sure. Here come the printers."

"Why, that's a printing press on the wagon," said Susan Augusta.

"Will Papa be with the printers because they print his books?" Cally asked, turning to look at her mother.

"Papa will be with his club, dear."

The press was printing briskly. As fast as papers came off the press the printers threw them to the crowd.

"Oh, I want one," said Susan Augusta.

The girls held out their hands. The men tossed the pages high, but they fluttered down. Then a gust of wind sent some soaring. One flew straight to the window.

"Read it, Mama."

Mrs. Cooper read:

" 'Tis done! 'Tis done. The mighty chain
Which joins bright Erie to the Main
For ages shall perpetuate
The glories of our native state."

Below the window the crowd was reading the verses, too.

"Do you think James Fenimore Cooper wrote this?" asked a woman.

"Oh, no. It's not that good," her companion answered. "Why, Cooper's the greatest author in America."

"He's the greatest author in the world," said a man with a foreign accent. "My sister read *The Pioneers* in Swedish."

"My brother read it in French."

"I read it in Italian," said a little, dark-haired woman. "I understand he's just finished a new book, *The Last of the Mohicans*, which will be his masterpiece."

Then everyone began to talk about Cooper.

"He's the first American literary genius to be recognized in Europe!"

"Wasn't Washington Irving the first?"

"His success is nothing compared to Cooper's.

Why, Cooper's books are known in Persia and in Jerusalem, I've heard."

"*The Spy* had a wildfire sale even in England, although it's about our Revolution."

"I liked *The Pilot* better. How well Cooper knows the sea!"

"Did you see *The Pilot* on the stage?"

"Yes. And of course I saw *The Spy*. Both made excellent patriotic plays. I can hardly wait for this new book about the Mohicans to be published. It should be exciting."

"That is the Cooper family in the window. Don't they make a picture?"

"They are going abroad soon. All the important people in Europe certainly will be proud to welcome Cooper."

"I stopped here to watch the procession because I thought it would be the best place to see Cooper."

"So did I."

"So did I."

"So did I."

"Have you heard he is going to petition the next legislature to add Fenimore to the family name? He is doing it to please his mother. Her maiden name was Fenimore."

"Is that the Bread and Cheese Club coming?"

"What is the Bread and Cheese?"

"Oh, its a luncheon club. Cooper started it. When they vote members into the club, bread means 'for' and cheese means 'against.' "

"Here he comes!"

"Papa! Papa!" The little girls in the upstairs window clapped their hands. The gentlemen waved their canes to the girls. Stuck on the end of some of the canes was a slice of bread. On others there was a chunk of cheese.

"Hurrah for the Bread and Cheese!" the crowd shouted.

"Everybody calls it that," murmured Mrs.

Cooper, but not even the children heard her. "James calls it simply the 'Lunch.' I'm glad he's taken time to be in the parade. He's worked so hard on *The Last of the Mohicans*. It should be his best book."

The crowd was swarming around the carriage. Books to be autographed were thrust at James Cooper. Friendly hands were extended.

Smiling, he signed his name and gripped the hands of his countrymen, saying, "Thank you. Thank you. Yes, Hawkeye in his leather stockings is in *The Last of the Mohicans*. Yes, I'll write more about him, and Indians, and deer slaying, and the adventures of my boyhood. I'm at work on another book now. Maybe I'll write a Leatherstocking Series!"

"How Cooper's ruddy, outdoor face shows up among those city men," said the man with the foreign accent. "Who are they?"

"Famous Americans," a man answered. "Next

to Cooper is William Cullen Bryant, the poet. They're great friends. Next is Samuel Morse, then Fitz-Greene Halleck. He's a writer, too. Behind them is J. W. Jarvis. He painted a fine portait of Cooper and——"

The driver of the carriage was trying to coax the horses forward.

As the crowd fell back a cheer rose.

"Hurrah for a great American!"

"Hurrah for a patriot!"

"Hurrah for Cooper!"

The cry was taken up on both sides as the carriage rolled along.

James Cooper, flushed, smiling, bowed right and left to the cheers of the crowd. Then he stood up in the carriage and waved his hat to the beaming faces in the window.

"There——" Fan sighed happily—"the parade was, too, for Papa!"

Hawkeye
Still Lives

MORE THAN one hundred and fifty years after
Jimmie Cooper played and hunted in the forest
near his home on Lake Otsego, two schoolboys
plodded up the steps of a public library.

"Jerry, I'm going to pick the shortest book on
the reading list for my report," one said. "Isn't
that what you're going to do, too?"

"No, Carl, I'm not. I've decided to read *The
Last of the Mohicans*, a book by James Fenimore
Cooper," said Jerry.

"Is that on the list? Why, I've read it! It's
really thrilling—full of danger and fights."

"So is *The Deerslayer*. Hawkeye is in it, too.

Grandpa says that, as a boy, he loved all of Cooper's books."

"They must be mighty old, if your grandfather read them when he was little."

"They are, and that's why they're so good. Cooper lived on the frontier. He really knew Indians, scouts, and wild animals. His stories are about things that really happened."

A girl with a book tucked under her arm came down the steps.

"Hello," she said. "Are you here to get your books. I've taken out *The Deerslayer* for my report." She showed them the book.

"No fair, Babs. I wanted to read that one," said Carl, a little annoyed.

"*The Deerslayer* is not a book for girls," Jerry added quickly.

"I'm sure I'll like it," Babs replied. "I liked *The Last of the Mohicans*, and last summer I saw Hawkeye!"

190

"Oh, he died ages ago," protested Jerry.

"I mean I saw the statue. Mother and Father took me to Cooperstown, New York. I saw the woods, Lake Otsego, Council Rock, and a big statue of Leatherstocking."

"Leatherstocking?" Carl looked puzzled.

"That's another name for Hawkeye," Jerry explained. "He always wore long leather leg-

191

gings, like stockings. The books about him are called *The Leatherstocking Tales.*"

"Oh, I remember now," admitted Carl.

"Good-by," Barbara said. She called back, "There is still a copy of *The Last of the Mohicans* in the library."

Carl and Jerry looked at each other.

"Hurry," Carl exclaimed. "We don't want to miss Hawkeye!"

The boys raced up the rest of the steps two at a time.

More About This Book

WHEN JAMES FENIMORE COOPER LIVED

1789   JAMES FENIMORE COOPER WAS BORN IN BUR-
      LINGTON, NEW JERSEY, SEPTEMBER 15.

There were 11 states in the Union.

George Washington was President.

The population of the country was about
3,910,000.

1790–   THE COOPER FAMILY LIVED IN COOPERSTOWN
1800   ON THE SHORE OF LAKE OTSEGO, NEW YORK.

The first banking system was established in the
United States, 1791.

Eli Whitney invented the cotton gin, 1793.

John Adams was President, 1797-1801.

George Washington died, 1799.

1800–   JIMMIE ATTENDED DR. THOMAS ELLISON'S
1805   SCHOOL AND YALE UNIVERSITY.

Thomas Jefferson was President, 1801-1809.

The United States bought the Louisiana Terri-
tory from France, 1803.

| 1806–
1811 | COOPER SERVED AS A SAILOR AND MIDSHIPMAN IN THE NAVY. |

Zebulon Pike explored the area known as Kansas, Colorado, and New Mexico, 1806.

Robert Fulton built the "Clermont," first practical steamboat, 1807.

James Madison was President, 1809-1817.

| 1811–
1820 | COOPER LIVED ON A FARM IN WESTCHESTER COUNTY, NEW YORK. |

The War of 1812 was fought, 1812-1815.

"The Star-Spangled Banner" was written, 1814.

The first account of the Lewis and Clark Expedition was published, 1814.

James Monroe was President, 1817-1825.

Construction of the Erie Canal was started, 1817.

Florida was purchased from Spain, 1819.

The first steamship crossed the Atlantic, 1819.

| 1820–
1833 | COOPER STARTED HIS LITERARY CAREER. |

The Monroe Doctrine was issued, 1823.

The Erie Canal was completed, 1825.

John Quincy Adams was President, 1825-1829.

194

1833–
1851   COOPER LIVED AND WROTE IN COOPERSTOWN.

Andrew Jackson was President, 1829-1837.

Peter Cooper built the first steam locomotive in the United States, 1830.

1851   JAMES FENIMORE COOPER DIED, SEPTEMBER 14.

There were 31 states in the Union.

The population of the country was about 23,255,000.

DO YOU REMEMBER?

1. What was Jimmy doing when the story began?

2. How did the Coopers and their neighbors prepare for an Indian attack?

3. Where did Jimmy go to look for his dog Frisk?

4. What kind of festival did Mr. Shipman say the Indians were preparing to celebrate?

5. Who was Mr. Talleyrand and how did he entertain the children?

6. Who was Jimmie's friend Koogah?

7. How did Koogah and the two Indians kill the threatening panther?

8. What poem did Jimmy recite during the entertainment at Master Cory's school?

9. Why did Jimmy and Charles have a fight and how did it end?

10. How did Judge Cooper help the community to celebrate the Fourth of July?

11. How did Jimmy get the name Fenimore?

12. What exciting experience did Jimmie have with Indians on the night of the housewarming?

13. Where did Jimmy go away to school?

14. What important position did James Fenimore Cooper have with Governor Clinton?

15. Why did Cooper decide to write his first novel *Precaution*?

16. How did he come to write the patriotic American book called *The Spy*?

17. What other important books did he write?

IT'S FUN TO LOOK UP THESE THINGS

1. Where was Cooperstown on Lake Otsego, where Cooper lived as a boy?

2. What important historical events took place when Cooper was a boy?

3. What Indian tribes lived in New York State in Cooper's time?

4. Which of Cooper's novels include stories about American Indians?

5. Which of Cooper's books are most popular and most widely read today?

6. What other famous American authors lived at the same time as Cooper?

INTERESTING THINGS YOU CAN DO

1. Write a short story telling how people lived when Cooper was a boy.

2. Draw a map to show where Cooperstown and Lake Otsego are located.

3. Make a list of Cooper's most popular books and tell why each became popular.

4. Collect illustrations from some of Cooper's books for a display on the bulletin board.

5. Read one of Cooper's books and write a short summary for the class.

6. Make a drawing to show something about Cooper's life or something in one of his books.

OTHER BOOKS YOU MAY ENJOY READING

DeWitt Clinton: Boy Builder, Mabel Cleland Widdemer. Trade and School Editions, Bobbs-Merrill.

Erie Canal, The, Samuel Hopkins Adams. Trade Edition, Random House, School Edition, Hale.

Frontier Living, Edwin Tunis. World.

George Washington's World, 1732-1799, Geneveive Foster. Scribner's.

Historic Boyhoods, Rupert Sargent Holland. George W. Jacobs.

Old New York Frontier, The, Francis Whiting Halsey. Scribner's.

INTERESTING WORDS IN THIS BOOK

aspen (ăs′pĕn) : kind of poplar tree whose leaves tremble in the faintest breeze

brand: burning piece of wood

calico (kăl′ĭ kō) : cotton cloth, usually printed with figured or flowered patterns

chandelier (shăn′dĕ lēr′) : lighting fixture hanging from the ceiling and having several branches

198

corduroy (kôr'dŭ roi) : road made of logs laid cross-wise

doleful (dōl'fo͞ol) : sad, gloomy

dominoes (dŏm'ĭ nōz) : flat, oblong, dotted pieces of wood or bone used in playing a game

duplicate (dū'plĭ kȧt) : something exactly like another

embroidered (ĕm broi'dĕrd) : decorated with fancy needlework

excitable (ĕk sīt'ȧ b'l) : easily aroused mentally or emotionally

flotilla (flȯ tĭl'ȧ) : fleet of small vessels.

gorge (gôrj) : swallow greedily, stuff

loitering: lingering, sauntering

moderate (mŏd'ẽr ĭt) : limited, medium

persuade (pẽr swād') : win over to a point of view, convince by argument

powwow: Indian feast or dance

prey (prā) : animal hunted or killed by another animal for food

retreat: act of withdrawing or retiring

seining (sān'ĭng) : fishing with a large net equipped with sinkers and floats

settle (sĕt′l) : wooden bench with arms and high back built over a boxlike chest

sheath (shēth) : close-fitting cover or case for a hunting knife

skiffs: small, light rowboats

snuff (snŭf) : tobacco powdered for inhaling through the nose

spar (spär) : mast, yard, boom on a ship

spider: metal pan with handle and long legs

sprigged: adorned with twigs or flowers

sternly: severely, strictly

tabby: domestic cat, usually yellowish gray and marked with black

tamarack (tăm′a̍ răk) : tree or shrub belonging to the pine family

thong (thông) : thin leather strap

tidbits (tĭd′bĭtz′) : small bits or choice morsels of food

tittered: laughed or giggled in a suppressed or restrained manner

toga (tō′ga̍) : loose outer garment

wampum (wôm′pŭm) : beads made of shells, once used by Indians for ornaments or money